THE BOOK OF ESSENCE

Printed in the United States of America
Three Key Life, 2015
ISBN 978-0-9861921-0-4
Decatur, GA 30034
Jeffon@ThreeKeyLife.com

www.ThreeKeyLife.com

Book of Essence
Poems of Inspiration, Stories of Empowerment
and the Key That Unlocks The Greatest You

By Jeffon Seely
Book Design By Bobby Davis
Edits Done By Zak Elstein and Jonny Murdock

Three Key Life

Dear Eric,

Thank you for shining your beautiful
energy and abundant light into my experience.
I truly appreciate you brother. keep shining
With love. *[signature]*

This book is dedicated to the Essence within.

CONTENTS

steep trials before me
these steps lead to glory
patiently I endure
exploring
into a new state
I remain I
with my thoughts in a new place

I am

Section 1

Divine Awakening

The Beginning

The rotation of space allowed the light to dawn upon us,
the light that shines from us now reflects from us,
Divine.
The revolution lives inside,
where the mind and soul collide,
humility surrounds all sides,
all exists through our being,
our thoughts a guiding light.
Break mental cages, embrace equality,
it is not the individual's heart, cells, or arteries,
the Essence is a part of me,
a part of we,
a spiritual chi,
existing in harmony,
Forever.

Revelation of Love

Love,
brings clouds of hope over the barren desert,
illuminates and develops a presence that we must cherish.
Lands once deserted now see lush life return,
through harmony's rebuilding we best learn,
acquiring the unique ability on how to discern,
things that restrain from the things that empower.

Love,
propels our cells,
gives rise to our temple, our body, our mind,
love alone has been tried
love alone has withstood the test of time.

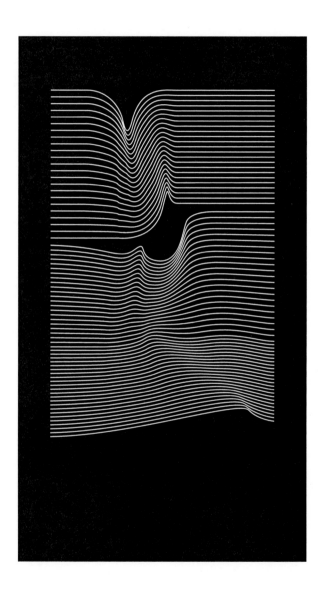

3

Eternal Reflections

I have a question, an eternal reflection,
do we see with our eyes or do we see with our mind?
If we see with our eyes what do we find?
Some seek happiness, love, and prosperity,
those only come from one's conscious activity.

Why do we compare others to ourselves?
Why would we want anyone to change themselves?

Realize you aren't of this physical world,
understand you are Divine Energy,
creating what occurs.

Realize you are breathing,
learning and receiving based on what you are thinking.
Understand that we are all one,
this earth, this life, this society,
creations of our individual imagination,
you see I, not God's manifestation,
rather witnessing the finite limitations you have learned to take in.

The Source and I are one,
you and I are one.

Visualize the universe, vast and without end
stars, cosmos, and life we cannot yet comprehend.
Realize your infinite nature,
remain in this state,
you are creative energy,

Flow to the Finish

What meaning could this world have other than the one we give it?

You are creative energy
you construct your own limits,
assembling the infinite,
Finish.

Flow,
where the eternal rivers go.
Your life is a piece of the Source
a miracle,
ask not for more.

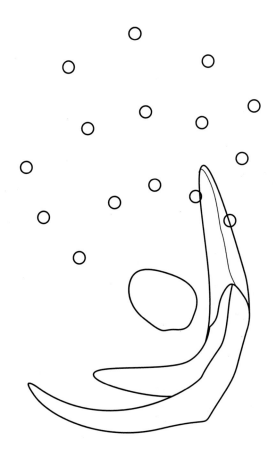

Must Be Done

It Must be Done,
it is darkest before dawn,
look deep within,
continue pushing on,
eliminate desire,
greatness is in store for all to admire,
suffer no more,
speak, act, and think with love,
from the Divine we are poured,
like drops of rain that fall upon every mountain top and plain,
we are meant to remain,
not to be trained,
it is time for all of us to obtain,
Truth.

It must be done.

Thrive

Speak spirit,
spoken words omitted,
from the depths of myself these words have risen,
from the dimensions unseen, though around us all moments,
seconds snap for millennia, limitless motion,
an Essence energy angle-less and unbound,
infinite speeds, endless seeds spread and sprout,
growth from within, learn through experience,
all that is known isn't based upon coincidence,
age is unknown been here for eons,
amongst kings, queens, thieves, and peons,
trees, past lives, rose with the phoenix,
seasons change, love is the power between us.

Moments of Gratitude

Grateful for all moments.

Times I thought I wouldn't survive,
revived me and got me where I'm going
alive.
We cannot die,
eternal beings,
this moment,
now
holds and has all meaning.
Born with all we ever need,
believe me,
things get rough, easy,
life reflects what one is thinking.
Thoughts and feelings, a dangerous mixture,
observe life and rise,
scenarios can switch from worse to great.
As you,
awaken to your enlightenment,
so vibrant it's reviving all,
providing us, inspiring us, reminding us
of love,
of the power to transform.
Avoid destruction, remain in the storm.

Two Things

Two things are guaranteed in life,
it's simple,
no surprise,
the day we were born to rise
and the day we die,
between these two promises people search for truth,
Unaware the answers exist within you

us, we and I.

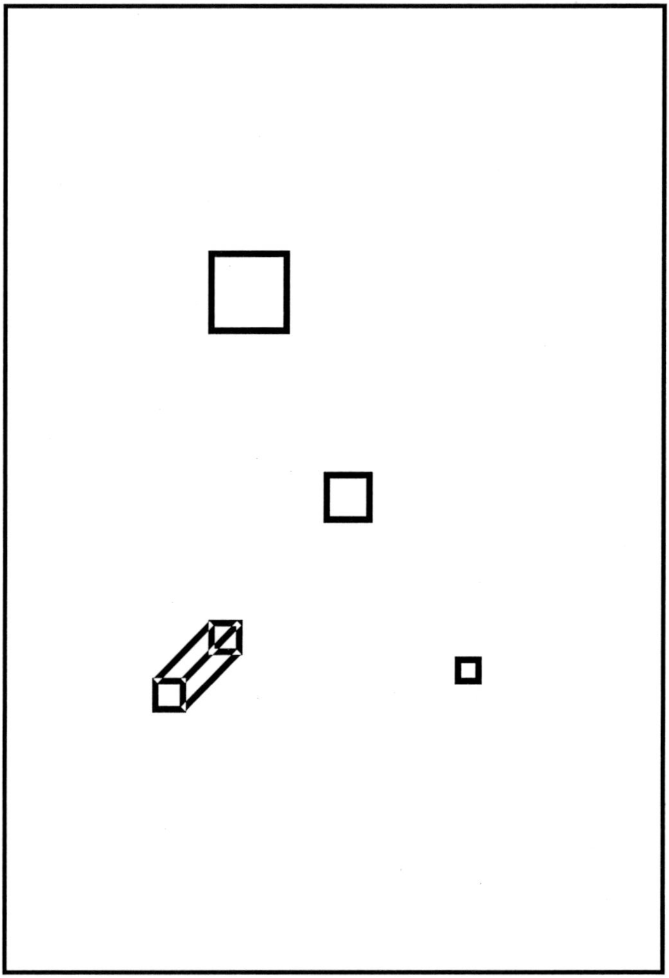

The Key to Ourselves

Our choice of communications shows the expanse of our imagination,
combine with the will to Be,
instill determination
avoid any specific organization which enforces separation,
once we separate,
conflict steps in,
and our consciousness is overtaken.

Be Patient.
Feel the life that moves about,
The divinity of glory exists throughout,
Embrace your connection to all
and observe the Divinity within.

Feel Gratitude.

The truth within is greater than words in books on shelves,
We need not seek
for we are God,
the keys to life rest in ourselves.

<u>Unshakable</u>

Looking out at the world I ask "What do I see?"
Thoughts sink deeper within my being to a place of make believe,
a connection beyond the grasp of imagination,
the one solid foundation through which genius is awakened,
the once real outer state crumbles as the conscious walls are shaken,
leaving me, the dreamer, in a constant state of creation.

Truth cannot be taken.

Up, Down, In

As within so without,
As above so below,
As you thinketh so you grow,
Transform thoughts into actions you control.
Often many of us go where others go,
taking a route we never would have chose,
on a mission for fulfillment,
on the search for our gold,
we realize our purpose
is the one we have chosen.

Step Confidently
believe in your dreams
open your wings
Fly.

Open your inner eye and see.

If one chooses not to embrace their Divinity
the door of greatness appears closed,
Fear enters in the body temple, the victim left froze,
while the road of greatness is right under your nose.

Step Confidently.
Speak Powerfully.

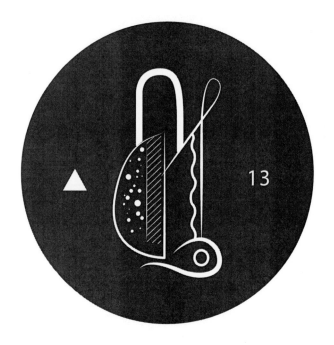

13

Start, Start, Start, Stop

Look higher than you've ever seen,
Explore deeper than you've ever been,
Once you reach that point
start over again.

Look higher than you've ever seen,
Explore deeper than you've ever been,
Once you reach that point
start over again.

Look higher than you've ever seen,
Explore deeper than you've ever been,
Once you reach that point
start over again.

Look higher than you've ever seen,
Explore deeper than you've ever been,
Once you reach that point
stop and look within.

Listen

I emerge from the depths of the gifted,
from the origin all life has risen,
my words float through air,
blessed by the light of creation,
open up your soul,
allow your spirit to listen.
Thoughts create your manifestations,
actions and emotions equal eternal reflections.
Behold and visualize where we are from, the tree of life,
many of us are still growing despite the lack the light,
while other branches have blossomed and become ripe,
there is no explanation of truth until it is time,
the truth is from within developed inside,
once this greatness has been realized,
all things heard, felt, and seen begin to coincide.
Listen to the voice that speaks of wrong and right,
listen to spirit within the people you usually pass by,
listen positively,
listen with love,
listen with an open heart,
listen, do not judge,
listen for the answer because an answer will always come,
listen faithfully,
control your mind.
Listen in a higher realm,
another point of position,
before you start to speak I ask you please to listen.

Inner Focus

Focus,
take a moment to pause,
reflect direction and follow your heart,
align yourself with the stars,
nature will not allow greed to be involved,
unless eyes remain closed behind doors of truth,
and the mind accompanies self gratifying attitudes,
improper use of the tools we have been given for progression,
corruption, brainwashed conditions,
we as individuals bring life into existence.
The power we possess can change the now.
Focus
take a moment to pause,
reflect the direction and follow your heart,
in order to start be patient, seek from within,
the same energy raises all life once the day begins.

AWAKENED

"4:45," Shelby says, looking down at her watch. "Fifteen minutes left then my weekend begins."

Slowly the clock ticks.shelby looks around her small cluttered cubical, checking her emails one more time then powering down her computer. She gathers the loose papers on her desk and stacks them neatly on the massive pile of paper already accumulating in the left corner of her cubicle.

"Finally, freedom," she says with a slight smirk as she clocks out and leaves her job. It was payday, shopping day.

These last two weeks of work provided her with the finances to finally purchase the luxurious handbag she's had her eyes on. Shelby exits the parking garage and heads towards the mall, beginning her payday festivities.

"$598.32," the cashier said to Shelby.

Heart beating with excitement, Shelby pulls out her debit card, exchanging 50 hours of hard work for a new handbag.

With the new handbag in her grips, Shelby anxiously races back to her car bouncing with exhilaration, thrilled to begin transferring the materials over from her old purse.

Joy and elation fills Shelby's car as she eagerly begins taking things out of her old purse and placing them into the new handbag. Content, and feeling a sense of accomplishment, she leaves the mall and heads home.

Head held high, new bag on her shoulder, Shelby heads up the stairs to her 3rd floor apartment. She enters, turns on her television and sits down with the handbag next to her. She pulls it closer and happiness fills her body.

She looks at the bag, then TV, and back at the bag, all the while beaming with joy.

Shelby flips through the channels, finally settling on one. A sound catches her attention as she hears the mail dropping in through her front door onto the flower-clad welcome mat in the entry way.

"Clank," the mail opener slams shut.

Shelby gets up, separating herself from her purse and heads towards the mail lying on the floor. Picking it up, she scans through each item on her way to the dining table.

"Bill. Bill. Trash. Bill," Shelby whispers, reaching the dining room table.

She opens up the bills, "Cable, $98.45. Power, $78.56. Gas,

$66.32. And rent," Shelby says to herself. "$1050."

She drops her bills down in defeat on the dining room table, realizing her inability to pay them.

Shelby drags herself back to the couch. With the weight of bills added on her shoulders, she slouches deeper into the cushions. She looks at her handbag, but bills fill her mind and her new purchase doesn't look the same. A heavy feeling sweeps over her as the happiness she felt moments earlier disappears.

Overpowered with the approaching reality of life, Shelby zones out, moving her attention from the bills and new bag, towards the flashing images on the television screen in front of her.

The phone rings.

"Hello," Shelby answers.

"Hey Shelb," Carie, her friend from work answers back. "What's up?"

"Hey Carie," Shelby responds. "Nothing much, here at home watching TV."

"Did you make it to the mall already?" Carie asks.

"I did," Shelby says in a defeated tone, proceeding to tell Carie how her day went from the highest of highs to the lowest of lows in a matter of moments.

"You'll make it through" Carie says after Shelby finished expressing her hectic day, "You're still gonna come out with us tonight though, right?"

"Tonight?" Shelby thought. "Sure, I need a break from all this stress."

"Don't be stressed Shelb, I'll talk with you more tonight," Carie says. "Come over around 9."

"Sounds good. See you then," Shelby says, slightly snapping out of her gloomy state.

9 o'clock rolls around and Shelby is dressed in her nicest outfit, with a dress and heels that compliment the new handbag. She leaves her house and meets up with her friends Carie and Yasmin for their weekly weekend outing. Their night is filled with their usual laughter, gossip, dancing, and drinks.

Shelby, full of smiles brought about by great friends, leaves the dance club and heads home. As she gets further from her friends and closer to her house, Shelby's mind slowly drifts from the smiles of the evening towards the thoughts that choked out her happiness earlier in the day; she again begins feeling the pressures of life.

Bills, rent, work, doubt.

Bills, rent, work, worry.
Bills, rent, work, stress.

These thoughts twirl through her mind.

Shelby enters her apartment, throws her purse on the dining table, and lays down. Lying there her mind swirls, swimming in a pool of negative emotions she slowly falls asleep.

The morning sun peeking through her window, Shelby's eyes open to the sunlight of a new day. Almost immediately, she finds herself standing in the same muddy puddles of fear she wallowed in the previous night. Burdens, stresses, and deflating thoughts fill her consciousness. Confused, overwhelmed, and slightly hung over, she reaches for her phone and calls her lifeline; her mother.

Despite her mother showing compassion like any good mom would, Shelby still finds tears falling from her eyes as she expresses her struggles. Her mother, always willing to help her daughter out, asks how much money she needs and deposits it in her bank account.

Relieved, Shelby jumps up from the couch with newfound energy, ready to enjoy the rest of her weekend. Though she feels the twang of anxiety as thoughts of the approaching work week enter her mind, she is free from the burdens Friday brought her way.

Monday rolls around and Shelby's in high spirits. With her bills paid and her handbag hanging proudly from her shoulder, she begins another week of work as a customer service representative.

Mid-week, Shelby's attention is taken off of her work and placed on a new jacket she found in the mall one evening. She imagines how it would look with her new purse. Thoughts of the jacket consume her mind as she continues her mundane work with a complete lack of focus. With her eyes set on the weekend, she breezes through the work week.

Shelby returns to work after another weekend of laughter, gossip, dancing, and drinks. This weekend, however, was free from anxious feelings weighing her down. There was one thought uplifting her, that of the new jacket she desperately wanted for this upcoming weekend. She knew the exact amount of work she needed to do in order to get it, about half a paycheck's worth.

Shelby's workweek was filled with warnings from her boss for her lack of focus, slipping sales, and customer complaints. Each day Shelby's boss was on her case for her progressively worsening performance. Shelby's spare time was spent at home exploring the same five TV channels that had been entertaining her for most of her life. Eventually Friday rolled around and just as Shelby was hoping for, her paycheck was more than enough to provide her with the new jacket.

Grabbing her purse from the back of her work seat, Shelby clocks out of work, jumps into her car and rushes to the mall. She enters the store with an intoxicating feeling, locates the jacket, rips it from the rack and hands it to the cashier.

"$479.35."

Shelby snatches her debit card out from her purse and purchases the jacket. Having duplicated the same feelings of excitement and anxiousness that captivated her when she purchased the purse, she found what she was looking for. She heads home and makes plans for her evening.

Putting on her new jacket and best heels, Shelby grabs her purse and heads to her car to meet up with friends for the evening.

Excitement pours over her as she enters her car. She puts her key in the ignition, turns it, and nothing happens. She tries again and nothing.

"DAMN IT!!" Shelby yells stomping her feet and banging the steering wheel. She tries again and again but her car won't start.

Shelby exits her car feeling defeated, tears begin falling down her cheeks. The excitement of the evening is long gone as she begins walking to her apartment. Her problems become bigger each step she takes, returning to a familiar state of doubt and hopelessness.

"Nothing ever works in my life. Why is this happening to me?" Shelby murmurs to herself as she enters her apartment.

She tosses her jacket and purse on the floor and lays down on the couch. Turning on the television, Shelby tries to flee from hopelessness. Scenes of wealth, consumerism, and entertainers temporarily distract her from the stressful evening.

"$654.00," Shelby says with disgust.

"Yes, ma'am," replies the mechanic, "You've got a bad starter and a bad ignition switch."

"But, I don't have that kind of money," says Shelby helplessly.

"I am giving you the best deal I can," states the mechanic. "It's my job to get you back on the road as cheap and safe as possible."

"I hope something works out," Shelby says, fighting back tears and leaving the shop.

She gets back in the car with her friend Carie who drove, and tells her the news. A gloomy cloud of stress hangs above Shelby as she arrives back at her apartment.

Entering her apartment, Shelby lies on the couch, clicks on the TV and begins her usual party of pity filled with doubt, worry, stress and unworthiness. She finishes out the weekend having found her familiar state of hopelessness and victimization.

The alarm clock sounds, Shelby reaches over to push the snooze button hoping to capture 10 more minutes of sleep. Moments after dozing off, the alarm sounds again. Shelby woefully arises.

Shower turns on, hair and body washed, teeth brushed, coffee made, clothes put on, Shelby rushes out the door with her 20 ounce coffee in hand.

Shelby yawns as she sits down at her cubicle to begin making calls.

"I hate this job," Shelby says to herself, "I never thought I would be doing this."

The day was stressful for Shelby. Her boss was demanding that she close more sales. Her performance had declined over the past few weeks. If her sales continued to decline she knew the result would be termination.

As Shelby spoke with customers on the phone, she could only think of the money she needed to sustain her daily life, the money she needed to pay her bills and the money to get her car fixed. By placing her attention on the money she needed, Shelby neglected the customers she was talking to. Customers ended up getting angry and hanging up. The result, her sales continued to decline.

By the time lunch rolled around, Shelby still hadn't made one sale.

"Three more weeks," she thought, "I have three more weeks until I am let go."

A deep pit of desperation was opening up in the center of her chest as she dragged her feet into the lunchroom.

The cafeteria was upbeat, as it usually was at this time. The top sales people were discussing the sales they had made that day. Shelby walked past them, feeling annoyed she made her way to the vending machines. She pulled out a few dollars from her wallet and bought her usual lunch; a bag of chips, a candy bar and a Pepsi. She joined her friends, Yasmin and Carie, at their corner table.

"I've got three sales so far," Yasmin says as Shelby sits down.

"Three, I've got four," says Carie, "I told you I'm going to reach that bonus this month."

"How is your day Shelby?" Yasmin asks brightly.

"Same ol' same ol'," Shelby replies. "Four hours, no sales. I swear I get the worst list of people day after day. If they would just give me a good list I'd have more sales." Shelby finishes and unwraps her candy bar, taking a bite.

"It can't be the list Shelb," Carie says hoping to make her feel better. "You've done great in the past. You got me this job."

"Well those days are in the past Carie. I have three weeks to turn it around. If I don't I'll lose my job, lose my apartment, and won't be able to afford my car." Shelby says taking a drink of Pepsi.

"You know we are here for you if you need us," Yasmin says, hoping to raise her friend's spirit. "My house is always open for you but I know you'll pull through. Let's go out again this weekend and forget about it all Shelb."

Lunch concludes as the women finish sharing stories of the previous weekend. Shelby stands up, tosses her finished candy bar wrapper and chip bag in the trash and takes her last bit of soda back to her cubicle.

"Hello, this is Shelby with Stancom Network. I am calling you this afternoon to offer you the best package we have available. I see that you were a past customer with us and I am calling to see if you want to reinstate your service. There are several promotions you can take advantage of at this time if you sign up today."

"No thanks," exclaimed the customer, "I don't like your service and don't know why you guys keep calling me. Take me off your call list please."

"Ma'am please don't say you are not interested. Let me explain some of our offers," Shelby pleads.

"No, I don't want it. Take me off your list." the customer says hanging up.

"F**k you too lady!" Shelby says as she hangs up the phone. She puts her hands on her head, tilts back in her chair, and bumps into her boss.

"So that's how you handle customer objections huh, Shelby? Take off your headset and logoff, you know we don't talk to customers that way. For cursing at a customer it is a mandatory 2 day suspension," Shelby's boss declares.

"Thank you," Shelby snapped back grabbing her purse and jacket from the back of her seat.

"I can't stand this job," Shelby says walking past her boss heading to the elevator.

"Shelby," her boss yells, "This is your second warning this month. If your sales don't pick up and your attitude doesn't get better we are gonna have to let you go."

Unfazed, Shelby continued walking as if she didn't hear a word he said.

"I hate this, but I need money." Shelby thinks to herself back at her apartment. "I don't deserve this but it is all I am able to get."

Shelby closes her eyes, feeling that pit within, her chest rises and falls. Tears fill her eyes as she lies on the couch in her one bedroom apartment, her prized possessions scattered about the living room floor.

Shelby's attitude didn't improve over the next few days, in fact, it got worse. Her attitude and outlook continued to spiral downward as the pressures of bills, work and life intensified.

Defeat filled her days and pessimism wrecked her weeks. Then it happened, the worry, the stress, the doubt, the despair, the negativity, became too heavy and everything came crashing down. The things that she once turned to in order to fix these problems, namely her material possessions, no longer provided her the value she needed.

"Fired," Shelby cried as tears began to fall, "But I've been trying so hard."

"Shelby," her boss said, "I've been warning you for weeks, I was hoping you would come around. I have to let you go because of your lack of focus, bad attitude, and poor performance. I wish you the best Shelby."

At a loss for words Shelby left her boss's office. Grabbing her belongings and taking the pictures off her cubicle wall, she leaves her job for the last time.

Back at her apartment, Shelby arrives crushed. Now, not only has she lost her job but rent is approaching, bills are due, and her car still isn't fixed.

"Shelby, we just helped you last month," her mother calmly says on the phone.

"Mom, you don't understand," Shelby sobs, "Nothing is working out, I'm really trying."

"Honey," her mother says, "I love you and I want you to be your best. You'll never grow if I keep bailing you out from these problems. Shelby, I know you can pull through. Sometimes we have to sink a little deeper than we want in order to remember we can swim."

"Whatever Mom, I'll figure it out myself," Shelby spits in disgust, hanging up the phone.

Unable to pay her upcoming rent and bills, Shelby's desperation grew as she was forced to move out of her apartment. Without a car she depended on her friends to help transport her belongings. Needing a place to stay she called Yasmin.

"Of course you can stay at my house," Yasmin says, "I'm working late tonight so I'll leave a key under the mat for you."

"Thank you Yasmin, things are so hard right now and I have nowhere else to go," Shelby cried.

"I told you Shelb, I am here to help if I can," Yasmin said hoping to cheer her friend up, "I'll see you later tonight, make yourself at home."

Shelby enters Yasmin's house, dragging her luggage behind her. Upset and discouraged, Shelby looks around the dark room, overcome with emotion.

"How did I get to this point?" Shelby asked herself shutting the door behind her.

"Why me? Why is my life so hard, so miserable?"

The deepening pit that opened within Shelby has now become an abyss, consuming all hopes of positive experiences in her life. The darkness no longer sits at the bottom of that pit in herself, but has begun to cover her whole life, taking every good thing with it.

"Why? How? It's hopeless. I am worthless," these heavy feelings sweep over Shelby, as she sits on Yasmin's couch.

With her chest weighed down by problems, Shelby closes her eyes and submits to defeat. From this place Shelby tries to imagine how things could have been different, she tries to imagine how things could have ended up, she tries, she tries.

Amidst the wasteland of her thoughts, she imagines her friend Yasmin and finds a smile for a brief moment. Emotions and images of her current state flash in her mind, pushing the smile away and replacing it with a grimace at her current reality of no home, no car, no job.

Although quickly dismissed, her smile left a forgotten door opened.

A light peeked out from the crack under the door. A sliver of light in a sea of black. Drawn towards this light, Shelby inched closer. Cautiously approaching the door, Shelby slowly opened it, light burst through the darkness as she slowly squeezed through.

On the other side, Shelby found herself consumed by light. Not knowing what the room was, she looked around and evaluated what she saw. Unable to find any walls and not able to pinpoint the source of light, there she stood transfixed.

She took a deep breath, pulling light into her lungs. The light filled her being, bringing with it warmth and peace.

As she took deep breaths, the light of this room slowly began to fade. Soon Shelby found herself in her old apartment. Everything was set up as it had been before she was forced to move. Surrounded again by her old attachments, Shelby felt the light she just found flicker and slowly sink into that pit of despair within. As her light disappeared, she watched as the possessions that she once turned to for peace and comfort began to sink into the same pit until they were fully consumed.

Shelby watched as all the things that she once valued or cared about were pulled into the pit.

She stood in emptiness.

Soon her emotions began to fill this nothingness. Worry and doubt stacked in one corner, unworthiness and fear in another. Lack, limitation and insecurity filled the empty space.

At first it was comfortable for Shelby to see the emptiness filled again. After all, these feelings have been her companions throughout her life.

Amongst the spewing of negative emotions there was still empty space. Shelby looked closely as small specs of light she previously saw began to reappear. These small dots of light filled the spaces between her negative thoughts and emotions. She realized she could fill this room with light just as easily as the negative.

Shelby focused on the little specs of light between these heavy emotions and watched as they grew. The more she noticed this light the more light appeared. Soon the majority of the room she stood in was light. She smiled.

Shelby then realized that she'd always been filling her life with something.

"It's just as easy to focus on the light, regardless of how small the dots may be, as it is to focus on the negatives or stresses of life," she thought.

She saw that she was filling her life with despair, worry, stress and doubt. These were the emotions upon which she focused. These emotions drained the light from within her and she tried to replenish that light with material possessions. These possessions provided a false light that fed and intensified this darkness.

"It is now my choice to feed either the beauty or the struggle, the light or the darkness," Shelby said opening her eyes in an awakened state. She sat up on Yasmin's couch and knew what to do.

"Focus on the light in my life," she thought, "Focus on the light within myself."

Section 2

One Breath

The One

In the beginning there was One,
a flickering light
off in the distance,
Infinite energy,
possibilities endless,
composed of love,
completely defenseless,
began extending branches,
true to the One,
exploring dimensions.

The One, the universe, galaxies, matter consisting of elements,
preparing for the only thing relevant,
Uniting within,
weaving the ultimate script
within which all life is written.

Take a deep breath
soak it all in,
We are all One.
Forever expanding,
never reaching an end.

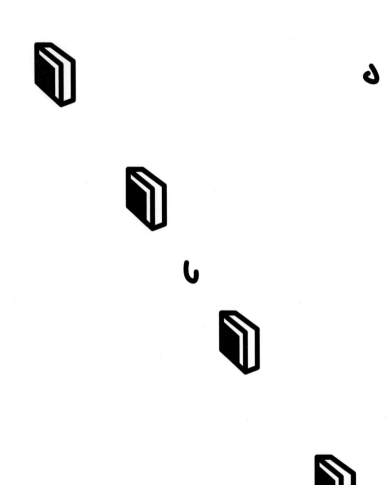

The Garden

As I wander to the perimeter of Eden's Garden,
my body transforms, my mind awakens, my soles harden.
Fully aware of my origin, the seed is not forgotten,
directing the roots to the Foundation from which they started.

United as One

We are One.
As we are unified and nourished,
humanity can begin to flourish.
The sounds of healing harmonies enter the heart.
A message of creation, establishing divine order,
bringing our chosen thoughts and visions towards us.
Providing hope for the hopeless, as we stand up for our earthly rights,
humility replaces ignorance, reminding us we live inside,
borders, boundaries, and society, forces which can no longer divide,
possibilities are endless when our souls unite.
We are change and we must take action now,
embrace the never setting sun, take refuge beneath the clouds.
The melody of the breeze amongst the trees,
the sounds of empty stomachs and heavy feet pound the street.
The intention is to awaken,all the minds of men,
tapping into the spirit where all energy began.
We are the abundant,
we are the difference,
made magnificent through our experience.

We are one.

One kind through one mind.

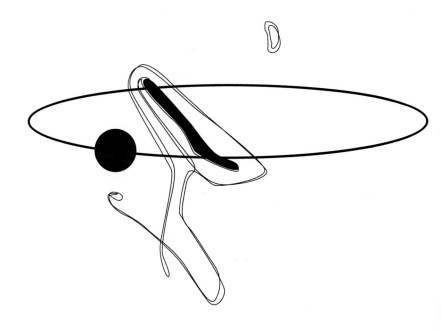

So This Is Life

So this is life,
pretend to fit into a system we're forced to live in, abide in,
strive in, and die in,
pull to the right for those sirens and duck low when we hear gunshots firing,
unless those shots come from a badge,
a badge that only the privileged have,
isn't the privileged just an ordinary man,
they breathe like us right?

So this is life,
stress, frustration, dedication to a job
constantly working in hopes to become free
freedom was given before the first breath we breathe.
Unaware some find pleasure in only physical things
overwhelmed with the lack of inner peace.
A deeper reflection reveals new truth,
all the things we've sold ourselves too
Fame, power, money.

So this is life,
accumulate debt for a degree,
a doctorate, good grades,
follow a dream another man made.
We must earn money for our family, our house, our bills to be paid,
stuck in the traps we've chose to create.
We all do what our authorities said we should,
their separation prevails in our world.
They tell you to go this way and me to go that,
You're too big for this and you're too small for that,
You're too dark for this and you're too light for that....

So this is life,
weekly we strive for spirituality, God, and wisdom,
just to return back to lust, money, status, and linens,
we choose not to see our thought pattern of addiction,
covering up under the blanket of religion.
We feel like we are the only ones heaven sent,
approaching others telling them to repent.

So this is life,
we teeter on the seat of creativity, ingenuity, originality,
we see our genius as a burden, an abnormality
we casually fall into rank,
a puppet in a play,
daily opportunities to give our Essence away,
9-5 everyday,
no questions.
Hobbies, aspirations, dreams
put all that to the side,
or do it after you get off work tonight.

We are not victims rather the manifestors.

We can search for many lifetimes...

What is it all?
Where is it from?

Until we understand,
everything happens now,
beneath it all is One.

Absorb and Give

The morning wind sings of the allure she has seen,
Awaken me to the brilliance this day brings.
The sun peeks over the ridge,
asking permission from the life below, to rise
content at rest, the plants await the light
though they love illumination, they also love the night.

Rocks embrace the moss as the dew covers the two,
the darkness of the night, fades to morning blue
The few clouds above kiss the now starless sky,
the light of the world returns to my eye.

Looking back at the landscape I see we are all one.

I soak up love, as much as possible
For I can only give what I have within.

The Shared Breath

Wind rustles leaves off trees into streets,
I soak in all life has to offer and breathe.
My lungs expand, I feel Saturn's bands,
made up of cosmos, galaxies, foreign lands.
Who I am is unknown, though given a name,
I travel as God energy, a Love unexplained.
I call myself eternal, floating on the waves of dreams,
forever connected to the universe,
I breathe.
Never alone, my surroundings contain me,
You call me crazy, but I call me you.

The solution we've been searching for,
that will release and set us free,
the answer to all our problems,
is found in this shared breath we breathe.

Magnificence

As the warm summer breeze carries countless seeds, the cycle begins,
life is endless,
time can never end,
the answers are exposed,
seek first and you shall know,
love is the power which allows all life to grow,
be still and feel the vibrations from your soul,
hmmmmmmmmmmmming, you back home.
I have seen the depths of the universe where the source of life resides,
not seen in flesh but with the eyes my spirit provides,
deep canyons and crevasses, lush mountain sides,
I can travel great distances by focusing my mind,
losing the conditions that I have learned throughout time,
now unconditional there is nothing I cannot find.
I meditate and create great landscapes flourished with love,
I eliminate hate, all are the light illuminated from above,
take off this earthly shell and know,
eternity has been here all eternity long.
Different experiences force us to rise to the occasion,
by understanding we rise our soul becomes awakened,
love cannot be taken, only given,
the one crucial element from which all life has risen,
a trillion cells coinciding with one another,
love is the link which completes this complicated puzzle,
love is the power stronger than any other,
essential are patience and love,
remain humble.

Love all as you truly love yourself,
lend hands of love when others need help,
compassion exists.
Allow this energy to radiate from you,
like a spring that sprung forth into a river of amazement,
love is pure and untainted with hatred,
your physical body is blessed and sacred,
materials have no meaning,
born upon this earth naked.
Become one with truth,
one with harmony,
one mind from the Divine,
in harmony we continue to move,
out of harmony we are confused,
blessed with all the necessary tools.

Be one with nature,
one with life,
one with the power that dwells inside,
one with all below,
one with all above,
most importantly become One with Love.

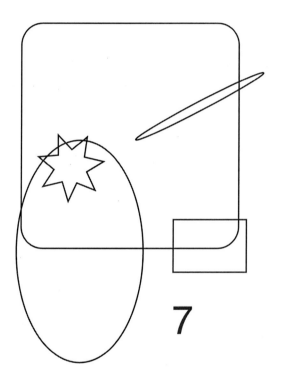

7

Deep Breath, Open Heart

Deep breaths send out energy
tuning in with the angels,
The heart center opens to eternal vibrations,
Changes are seen
you interpret your reflection,
once obvious blemishes diminish
I see who we are,
created in perfection.

The way we were made.
The way we have always been.

This perfection causes questioning on the way which we choose to live,
These deeper thoughts can effect your blossoming, for you need to love
but you add guilt,
Until the moment you realize who you are and you forgive,
Add your gift of light to your surroundings
The environment,
the people you meet,
the air you breathe,
your effects here are astounding.

Awareness of the abundance, some say is make believe,
If one is open to receive, it is heard in the words they speak.

How could I think of the world in which we live,
Without a conscious thought of the unlimited world within?

" I awoke to a sounding alarm clock, entering back into life. My eyes adjusted to the light of the room and my mind immediately began filling up with thoughts, ideas, and concepts that hindered my progression yesterday. These same thoughts have troubled me the past weeks, months, and years. Looking around my community I notice I share these struggles with many. Quieting my mind helped me realize I can anchor my thoughts. I wanted to know how much power I had within my own being. I made an effort to control the one thing that is closest to me regardless of where I am or what I am doing. I am still discovering the amazing ability of this universal tool. Everyday I become more aware of the power of my thoughts, the power of my decisions, the power of my ideas, and the power of my actions. I Am."

Looking outside of myself I asked why is this happening again,
When its me who allows these hinderances to exist,
Our thoughts create the world, our actions create our life,
Here to be reap the abundance while allowing fellow lights to coincide,
For we are not of this realm,
look beyond the flesh
Eternally we rest for all are truly blessed.

6 7

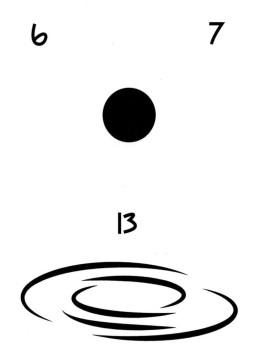

13

CONNECTIONS

Massive light poles stood above the cars passing below. Concrete buildings stretched towards the heavens as sirens and horns echoed through packed streets filled with fast moving people. The overwhelming sounds eventually found their escape in well-manicured parks with finely cut grass and evenly cut trees.

All this rushed through young Tanna's mind as she entered into the city, her eyes beaming with amazement. This was a big change from her upbringing in the rural south where trees stand misshaped but perfectly placed, and the grass fields sway the direction the breeze decides to take them. Where the animals come and go freely and the streams transport fish, rocks and fresh water just as the roads carry cars and the sidewalks flow with people.

Full of questions, Tanna fixed her eyes on the life outside the window as her mother drove towards her grandmother's house.

As they got closer to her grandma's house, Tanna watched as the environment slowly began to change. Soon garbage filled the streets and the lavish buildings that stretched towards the heavens were no longer there, instead, boards covered the windows of the small buildings and houses that filled these streets.

"Mom," Tanna's young voice broke the silence, "What happened to the big buildings? And why does this neighborhood look so sad?"

"This is a different part of the city," Tanna's mother replied, "I don't know what the people walking around have on their minds."

"They could at least smile," Tanna thought to herself looking back out of the window hoping to find another park.

The park Tanna was hoping for never appeared, instead each corner they passed had an abandoned parking lot or store with bars covering the windows as if it was holding prisoners and a large sign that said 'Liquor' on it.

"The same breeze that sways the grass back home," thought Tanna, watching trash moving with the wind, "now carries litter from the gutters out into the roads and barren lots."

Hoping to take her first breath in the city, Tanna began rolling down the window.

"Roll that window up, we're here!" her mother shouted from the front.

Reaching across the backseat, Tanna grabbed her small backpack filled with her most valuable items and opened the door.

Tanna's young mind examined her surroundings as she got out of the car. The first thing she noticed was one of those corner stores on the opposite block with a group of people hanging out in front of it. Looking back the other direction she saw a few houses with boards on the windows, broken fences and uncut grass.

"Are you gonna' stand there forever?" Tanna's mother asked.

Smiling, Tanna began walking with her mom towards her grandmother's small, one story house with a large rocking chair on the porch.

Entering through the small gate in the front yard, Tanna saw black bars hanging over the windows of her grandmother's house. As they walked up the uneven brick path, she noticed the same black bars covering the screen door. Examining the house even more, Tanna began noticing that the side of the house had no paint and the front yard was mostly dirt, with a large assortment of weeds. Just as she was looking up at the sky above the large porch, the screen door swung open.

"There's my angel!" Tanna's grandmother, Geraldine, exclaimed.

Tanna ran and leaped into her arms.

"I'm so happy you're here Tanna," her grandma said, hugging her tight.

Tanna could smell food cooking as she entered the house. The smell reminded her of home.

The house was beautifully decorated, filled with pictures of Tanna's mother throughout her childhood years, as well as pictures of her uncles and cousins.

"How long did it take grandma to put this all together?" Tanna thought, as she walked around looking at all the different bookshelves and tables bedecked with figurines, poems and sayings, each aligned with perfect precision.

Tanna felt comfortable.

"Thank you so much for helping me out mama," Tanna's mother said, "I hope my interview goes well so Tanna and I will be able to move closer to you and the family."

"It's my pleasure dear, you know Tanna can stay here anytime," Geraldine answered.

"I know that you'll do just fine. Any company would be lucky to have a person like you working for them."

"I'll give you guys a call every day. I should be back in two weeks," Tanna's mother said.

"Come here Tanna, give me a hug. I'll be back to get you as soon as I get back in the city. Be good for grandma and listen to her," she said, hugging her tight.

"I will," Tanna said in her innocent 9 year old voice, squeezing her mother even tighter.

"What's this for?" she asked, as her mother reached in her pocket and gave her a $20 bill.

"Just in case you and grandma walk to the store," her mother said, kissing her cheek.

Tanna waved from the porch as her mother got into her car and drove away.

"Honey, will you go put your things in your room while I finish fixing your lunch?" Geraldine asked.

Tanna did as she was told and then returned to the kitchen table where her grandmother had already prepared a plate for her.

"So what are we going to do while I'm here grandma?" Tanna asked, taking a big bite of her sandwich.

"Well," her grandma said, "I have some new games that we can play, I got you some new coloring books and have a few movies that you always love."

"Ok," she said, continuing to eat.

Tanna finished her food and took her plate to the sink.

"Grandma, can I go and play outside for a little?" she asked.

"No," her grandma immediately responded, "It's not safe out there. The only time you're allowed to play out there is if grandma's with you. I don't want anything to happen to you," Geraldine finished.

Tanna didn't argue, instead she went to her room and grabbed a few toys she brought from home.

Hours passed.

"Grandma, why can't I go outside?" Tanna asked in a curious voice as she was brushing her doll's hair on the living room floor.

"Because Tanna, this neighborhood isn't like your neighborhood back home. There are people getting hurt here every day. Shootings, kidnappings, robberies, it's not a place for a sweet girl like you." her grandmother explained. Tanna thought nothing of it and continued combing her doll's hair.

A week passed and Tanna hadn't seen anything outside the walls of her grandma's house since her mother left. Growing bored and tired of her toys, she asked her grandma every hour on the dot if she could go outside. The answer was always the same, "No." The reason never changed either, "it's not safe."

Her tenacity paid off however. Running low on food for dinner,

Geraldine finally had to leave the house to go to the small store a few houses down.

"Put on your shoes Tanna," Geraldine said, "Let's go to the store."

Filled with excitement, Tanna grabbed her shoes, her favorite toy and the $20 bill her mother had given her.

"Let's go grandma," Tanna said, opening the heavy screen door.

The light filled Tanna's eyes as they stepped outside, immediately Geraldine grabbed Tanna's hand, preventing her from wandering.

Making their way to the corner store, they first had to get through the front yard. Tanna saw the hard, dry dirt and she spotted a small patch of dandelions in the corner of the yard. Walking through the front gate, they proceeded down the sidewalk.

Gazing down as they walked, Tanna noticed the uneven, cracking sidewalk, feeling her body lean the way the cement slab slanted.

Crossing the street to the small store, she saw a group of people standing outside the entrance. As they got closer, her grandma squeezed her hand tighter. Tanna lifted her other hand with her toy in it and began waving at the young crowd.

"Hello," she said, walking past them. "Did you see the dandelions in my grandma's yard?"

"We just need a few things here," Geraldine said, rushing through the entrance and down one of the dingy aisles, "Follow me."

Grabbing the essentials needed for next week's cooking, they headed to checkout.

"Miss Geraldine," a voice said from behind them in the checkout line.

Turning, Tanna saw one of the young men from outside the store.

"I need $20 for some food," the young man said, laughing.

"I don't have any money for you," Geraldine said.

Tanna felt her grandma squeeze her small hand.

"I know you got money Geraldine," the young man said.

"I can't afford to give you money," Geraldine said, her voice trembling.

Tanna let go of her grandmother's hand and reached into her back pocket.

"Here you go," Tanna said smiling.

The young man slowly reached out and grabbed the money.

"You shouldn't be going hungry," Tanna said, looking up at the young man.

"Thanks," the young man said slowly as he awkwardly took the $20 bill from this 9 year old girl.

"You are welcome," Tanna replied.

"Grandma, you said to always give," Tanna exclaimed proudly, as they were getting ready to leave the store.

They stepped outside, passing the group of people who stood in front of the entrance. Tanna smiled and waved at the young man who she gave the $20 to.

"Miss Geraldine!" they heard someone yell.

Turning around they saw the same young man approaching them.

"Here," he said handing the money back to Tanna, "I can't take this."

Confused, Tanna reached out and grabbed the money.

"Why?" she asked, "I thought you were hungry."

"I'm sorry Miss Geraldine," the young man said in an apologetic tone.

"I can't take money from you or your granddaughter," he said turning in shame.

Back at the house, Tanna felt good. She was happy that she tried to help somebody. She was happy that she was finally able to go outside.

"Grandma," she asked, "Can I go and play in the front yard?"

"NO," her grandmother said, still shaken from the encounter at the store.

Late that night Tanna experienced a little bit of what her grandma was talking about. She awoke to yelling outside her bedroom window, then heard four loud shots and sirens. The news the next day confirmed the harsh reality Geraldine was talking about. Someone was killed just outside the room in which Tanna slept.

The next few days Tanna spent her time inside, gazing at the front yard through the window, spotting the same young man in front of the corner store. There were still three days until her mother would return to pick her up. Despite the news and violence taking place in her grandmother's neighborhood, Tanna's young mind had had enough with being locked inside the house day after day.

The following morning she made it a goal to ask her grandmother every ten minutes if she could go outside and play.

By the time 3 pm rolled around, Tanna had asked her grandmother over 50 times if she could go outside. Growing impatient, Geraldine finally said yes.

"Ok Tanna, you can go outside, but you have to stay in the front yard, and you can't go out of my view from the porch," she said.

'"Yessss!" Tanna shouted, running to get her shoes, ready to venture off into the unknown yard which was so close, yet so far.

Outside was a whole new world to her. The dry grass, weed-filled garden and broken fence seemed like a foreign planet, especially since she didn't have her grandmother's hand preventing her from exploring.

Tanna wanted to try and find life that was able to survive in this rough environment her grandmother spent so much time warning her about. Accompanied by her favorite doll, she roamed through the yard, astonished by all the life thriving in the barren yard.

She ventured towards the small dandelion patch she saw a few days earlier and noticed a small mound of ants working ceaselessly. She followed the trail of ants into the middle of the yard where an empty food wrapper sat. The ants swarmed around this piece of trash, gathering food from it and taking it back to their precious mound. Amazed, Tanna sat there and watched as hundreds of ants came and went from this one piece of trash.

Returning back to the dandelion patch, she ran her fingers across the dry cracked dirt, recognizing that the dandelions were flourishing in this inhospitable environment.

Picking a few of the dandelions, she made a small bouquet and took them to her grandmother who was watching her every move from the large rocking chair on the porch.

After giving the flowers to her grandma, she ran back down the steps, venturing into the other corner of the yard. A warm breeze began blowing as she reached the opposite corner, bringing with it a calming effect and reminding her of home.

Gazing up, she watched as the large cotton ball clouds drifted slowly across the afternoon sky.

"Hello sun," Tanna said, closing her eyes, smiling and raising her face to the heavens.

She felt joy surrounding her as the fear she'd been taught to have for this rough environment diminished. Tanna embraced that moment, the ants ceaselessly working, the beautiful dandelions sprouting from cracked ground, the warm breeze blowing through her hair, the fluffy clouds that peacefully drifted above her and the amazing sun shining down upon her face, so bright, so vibrant, so warm.

"Tanna," she heard a voice from behind her, pulling her from the moment.

"Time to go in," her grandmother expressed.

Tanna turned in frustration and approached the front porch. She opened the heavy screen door and reluctantly entered back into the house.

"Your mother will be here tomorrow," Tanna's grandmother said as she brought her a plate for dinner.

"Ok." Tanna said, looking at the food her grandmother had just placed in front of her.

"Grandma, can I ask you a question?" Her small but infinite mind searched for the words she wanted to say.

"Why can't all things be like nature?" she asked. "Today when I was playing outside, I felt happy and saw all different parts of nature being happy. Why can't everyone be like this?"

"Well," Tanna's grandmother thought for a moment, "Because people don't act as nature does. There is corruption, sin, and the minds of men and women aren't always thinking peaceful things like you do. That is just the way the world works my dear." Tanna's grandmother finished, taking a bite of her food.

"I don't believe that grandma," Tanna stated in a loving yet defiant voice.

"The whole time I've been here I've heard of all the bad things in this neighborhood, all the stories of the bad people, and even heard gun shots. But today when I was outside, I saw something I've never seen," she declared, then paused a moment while her young mind pondered.

"I saw the ants working together to collect food from a piece of trash in the middle of the yard. I saw beautiful flowers growing in a dry, hard piece of dirt. I could feel the wind carrying peace and saw the clouds calmly drifting in the beautiful blue sky as the sun was shining down on all of this." Tanna finished and her grandmother's attention was fully directed towards the insightful little girl.

"Grandma I think we are all a part of this happiness," she continued.

"How do you mean?" Geraldine asked in a hopeful voice.

"I mean," Tanna continued, "We are all a part of this happiness I saw in the front yard today, but if we don't look for it we'll never see it, and if we don't see it then we'll never know we are a part of it." Tanna finished, returning back to her food, unaware of her powerful message.

Love is the environment that encompasses all things. We breathe it, we work in it, we live in it, and we are forever a part of it. Embrace this love, this oneness and allow it to be the driving force of your life, for it is this oneness that all things come from. Prosperity, success, happiness, relationships, beauty, harmony, and peace are a direct reflection of this amazing love. Open yourself to this one breath we share. Open yourself so that love can flow through you unhindered.

Be One with All.

Section 3

The Power Within

The Power: Good and Bad

Misconceptions reflect false intentions,
Misinterpretations circles back to one's Essence,
Ego driven fundamentals give rise to separation,
From the spirit of the Divine which aligns itself with creation.
Creating a feeling, an awareness through awakening,
Understanding that things are never really what they seem,
Prosperity and increase is truly ours,
Through conditions and self interest Divinity is clogged.
Hindering the river of abundance,
the rushing waters have now ceased,
hot sands of egotistical belief now burn our feet,
that is until humility cools our soles,
the third eye unfolds,
and all that is mine suddenly becomes yours.

One Power.

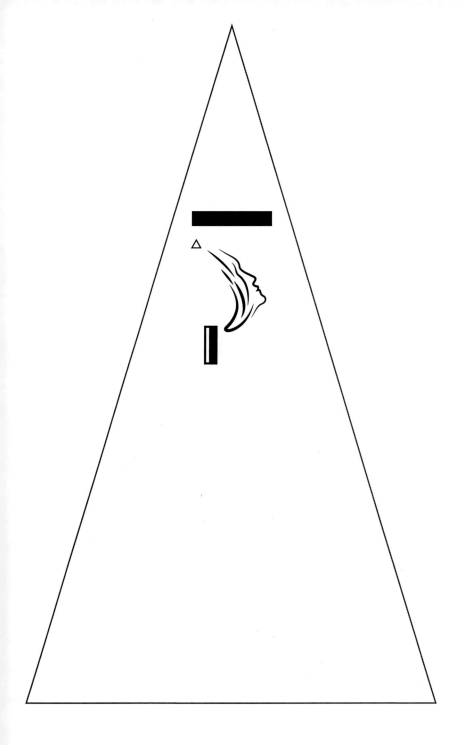

New Dimensions Within

Thoughts become life,
existence progresses,
tap into truth,
open new dimensions.

Divine eyes shine energy through our being,
Love and happiness is what we are meant to see.

Believe in your universal ability,
Release nonsense and blossom magnificently.
Separate yourself from all that hinders
Unite with love.

Allow your soul to sing the songs of eternal life,
let go of external factors and begin to live inside.

The Rise

Like a circle,
there is never a beginning, never an ending,
Man is his only opposition.
His mental conditioning can't hear deep whispers,
that ask him to Listen.

Through the abundant graces, we begin changing places,
into our true potential of being.
The transformation is provided by the foundation
built upon the Essence we all contain.
Plentiful magnificence, not based upon coincidence,
it is the seed we sow that provides the gift.

Together we stand,
Hate propels our demise.
Choose to rise.

Uncovering Purpose

An Angel descended from a star above,
Her hand reached out to me, inscribed with love,
with just a touch I could feel Her truth,
a feeling I can't explain,
a feeling I've never felt.
I tried to shun and overpower Her by the raising of my voice,
patiently She stood, patience was Her choice,
She was amazing, my negativity She embraced it,
I began to contemplate,
was I worthy of Her presence or was She mistaken?
As I inhaled, the answer prevailed,
The Angel showed me the power within myself.
Astonished,
I smiled as She kissed me on the cheek,
Once her lips touched my skin, into harmony I fell.
An elevation took place within my existence.

I speak of the force the Angel brought to the surface,
Love is the reason why we breathe,
Love is our only purpose.

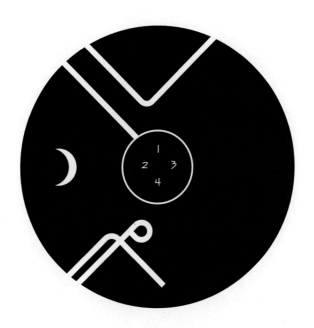

Glorious Rays

Embrace glory as it descends, open the heart to receive,
the Kingdom of the Ultimate equates to the energy within a seed.
Belief empowers thoughts, we begin ascension,
beyond the worldly realms of flash and greed.
Reverse the lustful circumstances, bring yourself to humility,
open the inner eye so you can finally see.
Most seem to think they alone have what it takes,
sprinting in circles to create a systematic fate,
failing to embrace this breath they've been blessed to take,
unaware of the power that lies in a natural state of thanks.

You are the destiny, emanating inspiration,
our creations lie in conversation,
once you feel this power praise will fill your days,
as you are continuously showered in Glorious Rays.

Exploration of the I in I

I search the Earth for a way, to find the page,
to flip past now to another day,
a day that brings truth to me,
disposing fake by the way-side,
then light can shine all the time,
simultaneously our souls align,
reshaping the etches of our minds,
Your life becomes mine,
and mine yours.
The walls of thought have discovered infinite fields,
what was fake then is now real,
new habits are built and life is healed,
only through the exploration of I was this revealed.

Knowledge, life, Harmony, life,
Love, life, Happiness, life.

Many say this is easier said then done,
I ask them where that idea comes from,
they point to one place, their imagination.
I can only say,
"So Shall It Be."

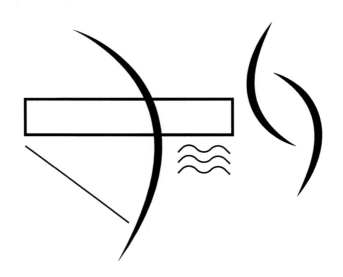

Inner Light, Outer Reflections

I open up my heart and love is received,
I open up my mind and I am given all I need,
I look within myself to find a safe haven of peace,
Slowly exhale this breath to share this light I breathe.

Genesis

The clouds broke apart to the sounds of an angel playing her harp,
from the stars she descended, white wings,
embracing a baby in her arms,
time paused.
God said Its goodbyes,
Kissed the child's forehead, putting Spirit inside.
God said, "This baby will be the joy of life,
they shall see the Divine when they look into her eyes."

And now the angels still stand at your side,
Leading you to the treasures that await.

You are love and inspiration,
motivation to all around,
your energy sings heavenly sounds
graceful melodies which part the clouds.

Remember who you are, always be yourself,
you are here to provide directions to those in need of help,
you are the light the world is waiting for,
embrace your expressions and share,
reach for your dreams,
look within yourself,
you'll find that God is there.

Eternal Journey

This life contains this light,
the power to illuminate the night,
spread's its message forever it lasts,
clues and guidance along your path,
a journey unknown except to the soul,
eternity speaks where the light flows,
an energy unexplained,
big as a planet, small as a cell,
perfect harmony will always prevail.
It is love,
the source,
the answer to the equation,
the struggles, the killing,
the hatred we face in this nation,
the tears, the wounds, the scars, the hurt,
love is beneath all the ills upon this earth.

Contained by all
unknown by many.

We

I am you,
in a vessel that produces an expression,
beneath the physical mantle I dwell,
within all, my energy continues,
the strength that allows us all to continue,
in the direction chosen,
the purpose unknown,
comprehension of meaning forms as we leap to different stones,
the answer will manifest,
contained by all is the key that opens the treasure chest,
full of abundance to be spread amongst us,
the dawn of a new era is now upon us,
tap in, you're the creator,
overflowing with potential,
faith is the connector,
attracting what is meant,
doubt not because your thoughts will always manifest.

Evolution Within

The revolution evolves from the seed that sprouts within,
allow the light to reach the depths where all of life begins,
truth touches the souls of those whose eyes are closed,
release the fierce hold that once intruded and imposed,
Can you feel it?
The realness, the reason why we are breathing,
overcome and succeed but only if we truly believe it,
constantly amongst us, about us, throughout us,
all of life, the microscopic, the galaxies and passed that.
Send the message for the energy is everlasting,
forever standing, spanning all that is and rapidly expanding,
recapturing space as light becomes the darkness,
life brought to caverns and other unknown compartments,
unsolved mysteries reveal the forgotten,
the real will surface from the depths where it started.

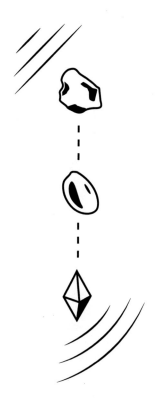

From the Depths of the Gifted

These confined conditions alter states of living,
a single component in this cyclical system,
biblically it was written, but the truth is forbidden,
because the truth will set you free.
Release dis-ease, allow the entrance of peace,
watch and see life's bliss as it should be.
From
the furthest star, connected by one,
travel endlessly to see, now, become,
manifest this moment as air fills the lungs,
purpose has begun.
The source is the reason for this decent,
to separate the Essence from the pretend,
the real from the fake,
peace from the conflicts we humans create.
Ascend from the depths of the soul,
a mystical occurrence,
light allows the spirit to blossom and flourish,
into potential,
abundant magnificence,
encrypted through experience,
enriched through sacred manuscripts,
we are, from all that is, and all that has been,
children of the sun, resplendent and glistening.
All is revealed, the observation of truth,
bringing you back to your roots,

From The Depths Of The Gifted.

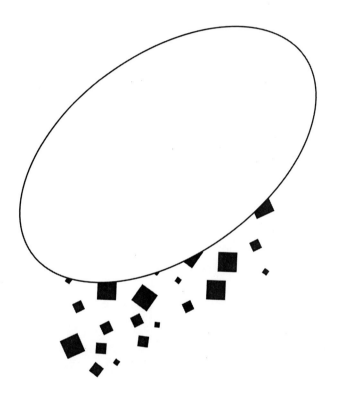

BENEATH THE MASK

The warm afternoon breeze swept its way through the crowded downtown streets. It swung around the corners of sky-scrapers, eventually hitting the back of a young man named Asmid. The sidewalks were filled with people. The city buzzing.

"This is a perfect opportunity," Asmid thought to himself.

On the corner, Asmid stood amongst a crowd of people. Business professionals, college students, homeless, fast food workers and countless others who filled the city streets around noon. Asmid always envisioned himself singing in front of large groups of people, but he never had the courage to do so. He'd been working on his singing now for years, waiting for the right time to share his voice with others.

"Is this the time?" he said to himself, half-heartedly preparing to sing.

He closed his eyes and took a deep breath. He searched for the courage to begin singing, or at least hum a small melody. Unable to find the inspiration he needed, Asmid opened his eyes. He exhaled embarrassingly and fell back into the crowd crossing the street.

"It won't always be like this,"Asmid said, entering his classroom, "One day it will happen."

"This is college," Asmid's professor warned, "These test scores are unacceptable, you guys need to put forth a little more effort."

Asmid looked down at the paper his professor had dropped on his desk.

"71, cutting it close," Asmid said under his breath.

After 4 years of struggling at a community college, this was his first year at the university level. School had never been his main focus, it had always been plan b. His main goal was to sing in front people, to step on the stage, and inspire crowds with his voice.

"Asmid, can I speak with you before you leave," the professor asked after class.

"Yes Ma'am," Asmid said walking to the professor's desk.

"Finals are next week. You need to get a 70 to pass the class," Mrs. Douglas cautioned.

In response Asmid sang, "'Mrs. Douglas, I hope that you see by giving me a C, you are doing your part in history."

Mrs. Douglas smiled. "Study a little," she said, returning to the papers on her desk.

"You're still here," Asmid said to his mother as he entered their small house.

"I'm heading out the door right now, I left some spaghetti out for dinner. Don't forget to help your sister with her homework," Asmid's mother kissed him and rushed out the door.

"When will I get some time for myself?" Asmid thought loudly.

The night was filled with the usual. Asmid sung while he cooked, sung while he cleaned, helped his younger sister with her homework, then sang her to sleep. It was 10 pm by the time Asmid opened his books up to study, only to awake three hours later when his mother returned from work.

The next morning walking to school Asmid was humming a new song he came up with the night before. He thought about his goals, he thought about his singing, he thought about sharing his gifts.

Standing on the same corner he stood on the day before, he felt anxious.

"I can do it," Asmid said to himself, closing his eyes, "Now's my time to at least try."

Asmid took a deep breath, pushing the fear aside. Still fearful, he took another breath to finally begin singing. Just as he let out his first note he was bumped from behind, losing his balance and a small, high-pitched peep escaped from his mouth. Opening his eyes he noticed a few people were staring at him. Humiliated, Asmid fell back into the crowd and crossed the street.

"Yo, Mid!" someone shouted.

Turning around, Asmid sees his friend Jared approaching sluggishly. Jared, slightly overweight and a poor student had been Asmid's friend since they met at the community college.

"I need your help man," Jared said to Asmid slightly wheezing.

"What's up Jared," Asmid responded.

"Wanna go with me to make some money today?" Jared said, finally standing next to him.

"I have class, but could always use some extra money," Asmid said cheerfully, "What's the plan?"

"Not getting caught," Jared says as they both laugh and walk off campus.

Stealing has been something that Asmid and his friends had gotten quite skilled at. It started in community college. They would steal textbooks and sell them to their fellow students. Things were going great until Jared, unable to outrun the school security guard, got caught. Since then they shifted their attention to the mall. With a 30 minute trip to the mall, Jared and Asmid can easily walk away with $500 worth of sellable goods. This had been Asmid's sole stream of income for the past five years.

At the mall, things were going good. Asmid and Jared were leaving the electronic store with a decent haul.

"Excuse me!" a security officer yelled approaching them. Asmid and Jared looked at each other, paused for a moment then took off running.

Asmid went left, bolting out into the large mall hallways. Running fast, he jumped and tilted, avoiding other shoppers. Behind him he heard a thud then a grunt from Jared. Turning his head he saw the security guard on top of Jared, pulling electronics from his pockets. As Asmid turned to run, he was immediately grabbed by two more officers. They escorted Asmid and Jared to the back rooms of the mall.

"This is quite a day's work gentleman. Too bad you got caught," the head security guard laughed.

"Damn fools, why don't you spend time in school instead of stealing from others?" The guard arrogantly questioned.

It was a bad day. Caught stealing, given a ticket with a hefty fine, skipped school and for the second day straight Asmid was unable to sing. He replayed his day over and over in his head as he walked home. He put his feelings and emotions into a small hum, which transformed into a slight melody. With each step he found words to fit into the melody and as he entered his mother's house, Asmid was singing an entirely new song he made up on the walk home.

That night after singing his sister to sleep, Asmid remembered his song from earlier, grabbed a loose piece of paper and quickly jotted it down. Asmid lied on his bed staring at the ceiling.

"I am smarter than that," he said to himself, thinking back to earlier when he was caught stealing at the mall.

"And school," Asmid thought.

"I hope I pass my classes. Please, please help me pass my classes," Asmid said putting his hands in a prayer formation in front of his lips. He thought about his mother and sister and the way they looked up to him.

"Please help me pass my classes, please help me get out of trouble, please help me with my singing, PLEASE!" Asmid begged.

Monday, Asmid walked into class unprepared for his final. His hiccup stealing didn't slow him and Jared up one bit, in fact they had a very successful weekend. They made enough money to pay their fines and Asmid got himself a pair of new shoes. The weekend's success took his mind off his studies.

Asmid sat down for his final and was caught off guard by how little he knew. He figured he knew one out of every five questions, guessing on most of them. Discouraged, Asmid arose, turning in his test before any other student. He didn't make eye contact with Mrs. Douglas as he dropped his final on her desk and walked out of the classroom.

He didn't wait for Jared that day and walked a different path home. Cutting through an older business district, Asmid thought about the course of the day.

"After such a good weekend," he thought, "Why didn't I study? My mom and my sister are counting on me and I can't even pass a class."

Asmid put his emotions into words, singing as he walked through the main part of the business district, eventually stopping at a small corner store for a soda to take with him on his way home. Leaving the convenience store, he noticed a group of business professionals chatting just outside the entrance.

"This entire block," Asmid heard a man say, "I knew I was going to own all of this before I earned my first $500."

Asmid observed the men and women listening to this man. They were well dressed and stood with reverence, a respect, a sense of awe, listening to the man's every word.

"In fact," the man continued, "Even when I lost my first sales job, fired because of my poor performance, I still believed."

Asmid drank his soda and inched closer to hear what this man was saying. He leaned against the wall of the corner store a few paces from the small crowd.

"I know what you're thinking," the man paused, "How did you do it? Can you teach me how you did it? How can I do what you did?"

"Well, I don't have all the answers you're looking for, but I do know that if I can achieve success, then you can achieve success as well. I've noticed the way your businesses have been empowering our community, improving it in various ways. You've been given a great opportunity to influence others and what you do with this opportunity is entirely up to you. So my question is," the man concluded, "How will you use this opportunity you've been provided?"

Smiles reflected from the business owners that surrounded the man speaking.

"I am very thankful for the belief you have in us," a middle aged woman said to the man.

"Very thankful indeed sir," a younger man chimed in.

Asmid took another drink of soda.

"I am glad that you're grateful, that's important," the man said, "Use that gratitude to propel yourself and your business forward. I don't have the keys to your success, but I'll share with you something I've discovered that's led me to mine."

"I want to share this with you before I leave," the man said closing his eyes for a brief moment. The crowd grew quiet, staring at him intensely.

Asmid inched even closer, almost directly in back of the semicircle of people that surrounded the man.

"My friends," the man began, "You must meditate on good things. Meditate on your dreams and aspirations. Feel and know that you're a successful, prosperous and abundant person. See yourself living life fully. See yourself centered and see your life as balanced."

The man took a deep breath and continued, "Use prayer as a way to receive guidance, to discern and overcome obstacles, to provide strength and to reconnect with the Source that awakes you each morning."

"And finally, you must study. Your mind is your greatest asset. Work on yourself harder than you work on your job or business," the man said.

"If you follow these three simple things, Meditate, Pray, and Study, your business will serve more people and you'll become more prosperous than you could've ever imagined," the man concluded.

A chant of "thank you's" rang through the crowd..

The man shook each person's hand thanking them, then picked up his briefcase and began to walk away.

"One last thing," the man said turning back around, "Do all that you do out of the generosity of your heart. When you better the life of another person, your life becomes better too." He smiled directly at Asmid, turned and walked away.

Asmid leaned back against the corner store building in a trance-like state.

"This is the first time I've ever heard anything like this," Asmid thought, "I've never seen someone command so much attention, I've never seen someone so willing to help out someone else."

Asmid pushed himself off of the wall and walked in the direction of the man who had been speaking.

"Excuse me," Asmid called out, approaching the man.

The man stopped and turned.

"Meditate, Pray, and Study? That's all I have to do to be successful?" Asmid asked as he got closer.

"Young man, if you can master these three things, you'll realize that you're the captain of your destiny. You can direct your life wherever you'd like," the man answered.

"These three things," Asmid laughed, "Life's much more than that, at least my life is."

"I already know they work for me," the man said, "Why don't you try them for yourself. You'll never know if they'll work until you try."

"I will sir, thank you," Asmid said smiling.

They shook hands and went their separate ways.

"Meditate, Pray, Study," Asmid kept repeating to himself as he walked home.

He replayed the conversation over and over in his mind. Asmid recalled the way the people respected the man talking, listening to his every word. The test Asmid failed earlier, had all but left his mind.

"Meditate, Pray, Study," Asmid said, entering his mother's house. Asmid went into his room, jotted these ideas down and immediately tried to meditate. Finding it difficult to quiet his mind, he rose to his knees, put his hands in a prayer position to begin praying.

"Please help me with my music, help me take care of my family, help me find the courage to sing my songs in front of people, please help me pass my classes. Amen," Asmid said, opening his eyes and looking around the room.

"Study," Asmid thought, pulling a book off the shelf, flipping through it, then setting it down.

"This is it," he thought, "Meditate, Pray, Study?"

Weeks passed and there wasn't a day that Asmid didn't replay the conversation he overheard outside the convenience store. He tried to adopt new routines in his daily schedule, setting aside time to meditate, pray and study. It was difficult. Asmid found that his mind never turned off, it was always thinking about something.

As a slow reader, he found it quite painful to pick up a book. The ones he did look through usually had more pictures than text.

With so many things that he wanted to ask for in his life, his prayers became similar to a wish list a child might send to Santa Claus. Overwhelmed with the extensive list of things he wanted in his life, Asmid rarely finished a prayer before opening his eyes and doing something different. Still, he tried.

Asmid began to recognize that the days he set time aside for meditation and prayer he was more attentive at school and with his family. Though he and Jared continued to steal, Asmid did so with the intention of helping more people than he was hurting.

As for reading, Asmid eventually ventured to the library and came across some books that peeked his interest. His readings led him to the teachings of the Buddha. He found that Buddha meditated daily, and it was through the process of meditation that he reached enlightenment.

The more Asmid thought about prayer, the more he thought about his grandmother who, as a devout Christian, always made him pray with her. Asmid also recalled his Muslim friend from high school and how often he and his family prayed.

Asmid wanted to find out why prayer was so important. This led him to begin looking through different passages from the Quran and the Bible. Browsing through the different religious books he found innumerable stories with prayer and meditation mentioned in them.

"Who are they praying to?" Asmid would constantly ask himself.

These books left him with a feeling that God, the Supreme, is something in the sky that looks down, granting wishes to some and punishing others. These unanswered questions fueled Asmid's desire to learn.

Over the course of the next few months, Asmid continued to write music but never sang in public. He continued with school but was still a below average student. Stealing was also becoming increasingly difficult. He began reading more and implemented meditation and prayer into his new daily routine.

"You're not going?" Jared asked Asmid as they walked through their college campus, "How are you going to make money?"

"I don't know," Asmid responded, "I need money, I just don't want to steal anymore."

"We haven't got caught in over 7 months 'Mid, we are making good money," Jared said, hoping to remind him of their success.

"I know," Asmid said under his breath, "I need to find something different, a job, start singing, something?"

"Singing," Jared laughed, "You've been talking about that since I met you, and a job, I've never seen you work a day in my life."

"I'm going to do it, I'm going to sing," Asmid said doubtfully, "but I'm not going to steal anymore."

"You're turning soft," Jared said, growing defensive, "We'll see if you say that after you see me making all the money."

"Whatever man, I have to get to class," Asmid said.

They shook hands and went their separate ways, Asmid towards class, Jared towards the mall.

In class, Asmid couldn't take his mind off of the potential money he was missing out on. His mind filled with his lack of finances, no job and doubtful music career. Asmid took a deep breath and focused back on his teacher.

Asmid found himself becoming more and more frustrated with his new discipline. It's been three months since he told Jared he quit stealing and since that time Asmid was broker than ever, unable to help his mom with bills and food for the house.

"This doesn't work," Asmid said to himself, thinking about his daily routine he'd been following for over 10 months. "After all this time and I still have no money, no success, I'm not any richer, and definitely not any happier."

The only change Asmid noticed was his mother paying him nice comments around the house, but since he hasn't been able to help her with any bills for the past few months, those comments were drying up more and more each day.

That night Asmid didn't do his usual reading or praying, he just sat, staring at the ceiling. It was already 11 pm, his sister was asleep.

His mind replayed the past year, school, singing, his mom, his sister, Jared, the man outside the store.

He recalled the three things the man told him to do, Meditate, Pray, Study. Asmid thought about all the times he's sat down to meditate.

"It has to be over 400 times," he thought, "I don't feel any different."

He thought about all the prayers he'd said each night before he went to sleep.

"Hopeless," he said to himself, "None of the things I ask for in any of my prayers have come true."

"And all those books I've read," by this time Asmid was reading about a book a month, "What a waste of time," he said, rolling over in his bed.

For the rest of the night Asmid replayed this same dialogue over and over in his head until he fell asleep.

When Asmid awoke the next day for school he didn't do his daily routine. He awoke, showered, and left for school. The city was busy, Asmid sang under his breath as he walked.

Asmid waited to cross the street on the corner where he'd stood so many times before. He thought about beginning to hum the melody he was singing moments earlier.

"I can do this," he said, closing his eyes.

Asmid took a breath and pushed out any fear that was within him. As he did this, he felt peace. Taking another breath, Asmid began to hum.

The melody left his mouth and filled the space around him. People's heads began to look for the singer. Asmid became louder, as he began to replace the humming with actual singing.

Opening his eyes, Asmid saw the crowd of people staring at him. Some stood with their mouths open, and their full attention on him.

Asmid smiled, slightly losing his flow, just as the light changed, allowing them to cross the street. Nobody crossed, everyone stood there watching, listening to Asmid.

He finished before the light changed again. The people began clapping, thanking him for singing, before proceeding to cross the street. Overwhelmed, Asmid awkwardly smiled.

"Jared," Asmid yelled excitedly, just entering their college campus.

Turning, Jared lifted his hand, beginning to hobble towards Asmid.

"What's up man," Jared said, shaking Asmid's hand.

"What happened to you?" Asmid asked concerned, as his excitement faded.

"Bad weekend," Jared answered looking towards the ground.

"Bad, how?" Asmid asked, looking at the large scratches on Jared's face and arms.

"Without you," Jared said, "I can't steal at the mall, I'm too slow, plus they know my face, so this weekend I decided to steal my first car."

"WHAT?!" Asmid yelled, "A car? We made a rule never to steal from people only businesses."

"Rules," Jared laughed, "You quit, remember?"

"True," Asmid said, "Why are you limping so badly, and how'd you get those scratches on your face and arms?"

"I got caught," Jared said, "My mom had to bail me out of jail Saturday night."

Just then, Asmid felt his heart drop, knowing that if he didn't quit stealing, he would have been right there with Jared. The only difference is Asmid would probably still be sitting in jail.

"What were those things?" Jared asked Asmid.

"Things?" Asmid responded.

"Those three things you do every day, those things that made you stop stealing? I need to do something different with my life 'Mid," Jared said, looking defeated.

Asmid thought for a moment, "Should I tell him those things don't work, that I quit doing those today?"

"Meditate, Pray, and Study," Asmid said, "I recommend them. I'm not rich yet, but a rich man told me about them."

They laughed.

"I'm glad you're safe Jared," Asmid said, "If you want me to help you with those three things let me know."

"It could've been me," Asmid thought, walking into Mrs. Douglas's class, "I could've been the one caught."

"Asmid, can I see you before you leave," Mrs. Douglas asked as class was getting out.

"Yes, ma'am," Asmid said, walking to his professor's desk.

"I remember our conversation last year," Mrs. Douglas paused, "Asmid, I don't know what you're doing different in your life but you've really changed."

Asmid smiled and said, "I don't know either Mrs. Douglas, today has been an interesting day for me."

"Well, whatever you're doing Asmid, don't stop. There aren't too many students who turn things around as fast as you have."

"Thank you," Asmid said.

Mrs. Douglas grinned at him and said, "Keep it up Asmid, the sky is the limit."

Walking home from school that day Asmid was floating on a cloud. It was as if he found his purpose. He knew he had the power within himself to make his purpose a reality.

"Studying, meditation, and prayer are key but that is not where the importance lies," Asmid thought to himself that fateful day, "The importance lies in the use of these practices to quiet my mind enough to connect with the Divinity within myself."

Astonished from this amazing thought he began a not-so-average day, a not-so-average life.

Section 4

Sacred Journey

Story of Greatness

I was once told a story of greatness,
how a man overcame mountains of doubt,
tread through valleys of adversity
always believing he would make it out.
The moment, now, was all he had,
never looking back to see what's been conquered,
understanding he could only be
all that's been
this awareness made him stronger.
Experiencing compassion, inner peace, and his personal flaws,
he began to see his presence in all that he saw.
A smile was all he needed,
it expressed all the man was feeling,
the trials and adversities reminded the gentleman
he is living.

<u>Please</u>

Believe in yourself,
have the confidence to share your Gifts with the world.

The Journey Inward

Life is always happening, in its glory we take part,
human potential can happen at any moment, blossoming from the heart,
we can participate in creation, open our minds to the messages given,
elevate above systems and begin living,
Right Now.

Not in the shadows of yesterday or the enchanted lands of tomorrow,
now is the Essence of life so right now cannot be borrowed,
For it is, a breath, a thought, a question,
who am I?
who will I become?

This Essence of life is where divine ideas are from,
in the infinite meadows of now, no two paths are the same,
whichever path we walk, they all lead the way,
inward,
towards the kingdom
"You."

Pathway to Gratitude

There was a young mother who lived in a corner apartment down the road,
A gloomy cloud of doubt filled her mind where ever she would go,
No money in her pockets, she was out of work and broke,
Barring the responsibility of three children to feed and clothe.

Everyday she sought employment but nothing was ever found,
Trapped in a prison of her mind seeing no way to make it out,
the voice within spoke but her problems screamed too loud,
any potential of hope was drowned out by cry's and pout's,
she looked towards the future, shouting,
"What am I to do now?"
She buries her face in the pillows at night to cry and ask how.

A few days later as she was walking to the store,
following the same path she has wandered many times before,
she overheard a man speaking,
Saying,
"If you don't like the life you live then change the thoughts you're thinking."

She couldn't forget the old man's words
she dwelt upon the meaning,
she felt this sentence contained
all that she needed.
She began to believe her life could change through affirmations,
incantations,
since that day before she falls asleep she says,
"Thank you for creation,
Thank you for prosperity and teaching me patience,
Thank you for my ability to be awakened,
Thank you for a great job and a stream of wealth that I enjoy,
I invite harmony in my life and ask that doubt be destroyed,
Thank you for this feeling of peace, love, and belief,
Most importantly,
thank you for helping me find me."

She said this for weeks and nothing really changed,
Except her state of mind, her attitude, and her faith.
Whenever doubt or worry crept back in her mind,
She quieted herself and said,
"Peace and abundance are rightfully mine."

She knew that within herself all her problems have been solved,
And once she knew this she immediately found a job.
A job that she enjoyed and a job that would provide,
A job that would bring more fulfillment to her life.
She reminds her children how important it is to believe,
Telling them,
"Never forget the power of saying,
Thank you,
and the wonders it has done for me."

Faith, Action and Manifestation

No more struggles or stresses,
no more regression,
accomplish the inner meanings intention,
faith + action = Manifestation
remain simple and humble,
always be patient.

Expressions Along the Way

Embrace greatness,
from the most blessed places,
a basic foundation
adapted from ancients,
communicate thought through words, dance, and paintings.

Sacred is this journey.

<u>Release and Become</u>

Enlightenment
being true to yourself is your ultimate obligation,
releasing frustration, unnecessary stress,
reflection upon your spirit's intention.

No questions, faith provides assistance.
Unless the fantasies hinder your vision
diminishes your dreams,
your conditions,
your society,
limits placed on endless possibilities.

You see, you are the Source,
connected directly to the master circuit board.
You are,
Have been,
Will forever be,
the only witness to your reality.

What we depend on as real is often an illusion,
a motion picture our imagination is producing,
dramatic twists turn down comical roads of theatrical emotions,
creations of your mind and now you must sort through them.

We have,
Everything.

Harness your power,
experience your scenes with patience,
all you need is found
riding that vibration.

All is Given

See your surroundings, embrace what you hear,
become aware of how you feel and the smell in the air,
enjoy the taste of life, savor your success,
stop to reflect on the previous steps to ensure this one is the best.
What comes next in your journey begins with this breath,
you are driving the vehicle to the destination ahead.
Don't place belief in the path but rather yourself,
when something is needed it shall be given.

Realize wherever you go you are already here.
Rise with the sun,
effortlessly existing from your I,
the One.

It is a pathway,
a track that people seldom follow,
embracing this day without the thought of tomorrow,
a gratefulness that all dreams are already achieved,
it all comes from this moment for those who believe.

This route is vital,
it is the key to the treasure,
this trail is important.

your journey's essential

Through the Void

I travel through the voids of sacred space,
observing possible futures I wish to create.
I see endless experiences and few I have done,
I slowly push the infinite aside and focus on one.

But for how long?

The moment will come when I have received all I need,
I learn not to hold on
and slowly release.

I become peace
and in silence give praise.

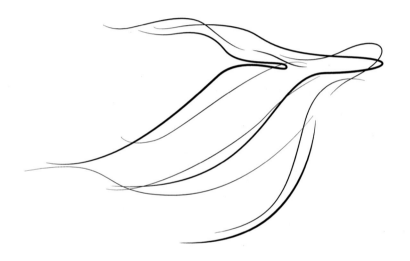

Melodic Melody

On the search for truth you will uncover the possibilities of today,
equate to your beliefs,
based not on the television screen or information you read,
catch a glimpse of truth and you are finally free,
enter your natural state of harmony.

The mind unclutters as the intangible floats to the surface,
dive deep within oneself
make worth out of the worthless,
live with purpose,
the Divine shines from all, into infinite sources.

The melodic melodies of one's Essence ring supreme,
it is your responsibility to express when the Source plucks your strings.

<u>As You Think, So Shall It Be</u>

I asked God how to love and It showed me Its truth,
I asked God for a queen and It brought me to you,
I asked God, "How will I know if these feelings are true?"
It told me "Worry not, as you thinketh, it comes to you."

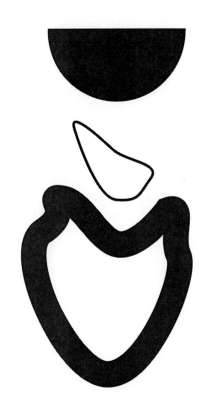

Here Already

There is no need to rush, we are already here,
it is only our perception that tells us hope is near,
beliefs of space and time create illusions of fear,
this moment now contains endless seconds,
minutes, and years.

The tears of the past were released the day they fell,
the past only has power if in it you choose to dwell.
One man spends his days in heaven while another chooses hell,
Neither is right or wrong, it's simply what you tell yourself.

The Wise Elder

A wise elder once said, this world is all in your head,
be prepared for the now because that lies ahead,
this moment is the only necessity,
this moment creates all destiny.
Communications between your self and your true being,
it is the voice of love that is always speaking,
take heed to the whispers, the spirit amidst yourself,
the origin of truth that surfaces from the depths

of your soul,
from the Light.

Sounds of the Voyage

Have you heard the peace from the river flowing downstream,
or felt the chills from the words of a fellow human being,
love radiates from the melodies birds sing,
eternal is life, seek out its meaning.

We are of nature, the ultimate creators,
tap back to the roots of our ancient ancestors,
the voices still rise from the seat of the soul,
most haven't realized the amount of power they hold,
surround yourself with the sounds, you wish to see surface,
understand love is all and you will find your purpose,
be humble,
time is forever,
immeasurable,
treat life with respect
speak impeccable.

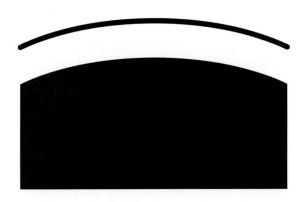

THE JOURNEY

The warm morning sun gently rose above the Rocky Mountains lining my hometown of Salt Lake City, Utah. The early morning sunbeams peeking through my blinds traced across the floor before landing upon my face. My eyes slowly opened.

Sitting up in bed, I noticed my camping materials leaning against my bedroom wall as I shook the morning cobwebs from my mind. Jumping out of bed I realized today was the day I was setting out to accomplish one of my goals, hiking Twin Peaks.

"I've been waiting for this," I said to myself, rushing up the stairs to shower before the early morning expedition. Finishing my shower and heading to the kitchen table, I thought about the massive peaks that had caught my attention since I was a young boy. The massive peaks were always out of my reach but always within my view.

"Today is the day," my Grandpa said from the kitchen table, "You'll love the view from there J.J."

"Thanks Gramps," I responded, "I'm glad you have the camping tools that I need to make it up and back."

Turning to look out of our kitchen window, I gazed up at the massive Wasatch Front Mountains that had greeted me each day after awaking.

"Are you nervous?" my Grandma asked, bringing me a bowl of shredded wheat.

"Not today Grandma," I replied, "I've always wanted to see what the valley looks like from up there."

Being the kind, caring, and slightly worrisome Grandmother that she is, she made sure that my small 14 year old body had everything it could ever need to complete this 3 day excursion into the wild packed snuggly in my backpack.

I didn't have the newest, lightest, or best camping materials, but I eagerly packed more than was necessary for this voyage that I'd been awaiting for years.

I rolled my heavy sleeping bag up and strapped my unique, well-worn tent to the base of my backpack, then loaded my mess kit, flashlight and dehydrated food into the main compartment which smelt mildly of mildew.

"I'm ready to head out Grandma," I said pushing the last tools needed for my excursion into the side pockets of my bag before tying my oversized boots.

This trip was one we'd been planning for weeks now. Every summer, the scouts who attended the church I was a part of set out on a 3 day adventure into the Utah wilderness.

Throwing my pack in the back of the truck, we set out to meet up with the scoutmaster and the other kids who would be joining me on the hike. Excitement filled my body as I envisioned spending time in nature and standing atop one of the tallest peaks around.

Pulling into the church parking lot, my excitement casually turned into mild jealousy, bringing me back to reality. My fellow hikers and friends were already there waiting, sitting on top of their latest and greatest outdoor equipment.

Grabbing my backpack from the truck, I realized that my hiking equipment outdated everyone's by decades. With my heart set on completing this journey, I pushed aside the jealousy, reminding myself of the view my Grandpa spoke of at the kitchen table that morning. I joined my hiking companions.

"All prepared gentleman?" Steve the scoutmaster yelled while loading everyone's backpacks.

"All prepared," we shouted, piling into the van that would transport us up the canyon and to the trailhead.

Traveling up the canyon and into this immaculate mountain range, the city streets were quickly replaced with clear streams and green leaves. The tall peaks grew in size as we continued driving deeper into the canyon.

"Gentlemen," Steve shouted from the front, "Before we get to the trailhead, let's review the things that you must look out for during our hike."

"First, keep an eye out for animals," the scoutmaster hollered. "There are snakes in these hills, but most importantly be aware of black bears and mountain lions. If one of those get you, you won't stand a chance."

"Second, keep your eyes open for the plants we've been studying; primarily poison oak, poison ivy and stinging nettle. The final thing is to know that it will be cold up there when the sun goes down. Even though we are in the heat of summer in the valley, there is still snow on the elevated peaks."

"We're prepared Steve," Ryan, an older scout listening to the scoutmaster's warnings half-heartedly, shouted from the back.

"I'm prepared," I thought to myself as we continued up the windy mountain roads. "I'll make it to the top."

After driving for a little over an hour, we finally arrived at the trailhead.

"This is where we'll begin," Steve informed us, "Remember all that we've been practicing while you're up there. Keep your eyes open and be aware of the risks."

Before jumping out of the van I made sure my heavy boots were tied tight. I grabbed my heavy backpack out of the back and threw it over my small shoulders. Taking a swig of water from my canteen, I began my trek into the mountains.

Gradual inclines slowly took us higher. Switchback trails provided us with time to get our bodies accustomed to the rough terrain that lay ahead. Looking around the beautiful mountainside, I noticed the trees, the unique brush and plants standing proudly in the afternoon sun. Butterflies danced at our sides while bees buzzed from flower to flower.

In the midst of nature, my canteen was becoming my best friend, swigging from it each time I started walking up a steep grade.

My mind and heart were set on the goal ahead, the summit that would be our camp for the night.

"Incredible," I thought to myself reaching higher elevations, pausing often to turn around and look back down the steep grades we'd overcome.

Two hours into the hike something stood out. Looking ahead I noticed that the older kids were not only bigger and stronger than me, but their lighter equipment made their journey that much easier.

Being that these were the older, cooler kids, I pushed myself even harder to keep up with their pace. Trying to join in on their conversations.

Looking behind us I saw two of the more heavy set kids lagging behind. Following those two, Steve the scoutmaster brought up the rear of the pack, encouraging the stragglers as well as keeping a slow but steady pace so we could all complete the hike together.

Unwilling to be with the slow pokes, I pushed my body to remain one of the trailblazers.

Hours passed.

The gap between the older kids and myself gradually widened, but as I had realized early in my journey the more I pushed myself to keep up with them, the more exhausted I became. This was causing me to stop to rest more and more. Each time I did, the older kids' frustration grew. After a few of these extended breaks they continued on without me while I sat atop a rock, drinking from my canteen.

Sitting there by myself in the heart of nature, I realized that while I was pushing myself to keep up with the older boys, the distance between the slower group and myself was greater than ever.

Standing up, I adjusted the backpack sitting snuggly on my shoulders and pushed forward. My pace, though slower than the older kids was still faster than the slower group behind me. I soon found myself walking alone amongst the immense forest I so eagerly wanted to explore.

Walking by myself, my mind wandered. Hiking at a pace that was convenient to me and utilizing the much welcomed shade, I was able to rest often and enjoy the cool fresh water of my canteen. I also enjoyed the apple slices my Grandma had so lovingly tucked away in my large backpack.

These breaks were becoming increasingly frequent as the higher I got, the more difficult the terrain and thinner the air became.

Late in the day, even though I was able to sit often to rest my legs and replenish my body, exhaustion washed over me. I no longer looked forward to reaching the top of the peaks, all I wanted to do was to reach base camp and rest for the evening.

Time ticked forward, finding myself trekking up rocky embankments and slick muddy paths where small springs had slowly washed away sections of the established trail.

The setting sun brought with it a calming effect. I knew that I was less than two hundred yards from the older kids who must have already reached camp for the night.

I stopped for a moment, looking up at the steep trail before me. It was the final obstacle of the day. It was all that separated me from the safety of camp.

Sitting to gain my composure before completing this final push, I thought about waiting for the slow pokes who were about 30 minutes behind me.

"I have to rest," I told myself finding a cozy seat on a fallen tree.

Reaching for my canteen, I noticed that my water was running low from all the consumption earlier in the day when I was working through much less difficult inclines and obstacles.

Untwisting my canteen, I took the final gulp of my water before tightening the cap back on.

Arising with my backpack strapped on tight, my legs trembled under the weight which felt as though I'd thrown a couple stones in my pack for good measure. Finding my footing, I picked up a walking stick I'd found and slowly began putting one foot in front of the other.

Legs burning, heart pounding, I kept my head held high with my eyes focused on the top of the incline where I could see the trail begin to even out.

With each step I took, the laughter and talking from the older kids above grew louder.

"I can do it, I can do it," I told myself rounding the final bend of the trail. Nearing the top, my legs were shouting at me to sit down and sweat poured from my brow. Unwilling to give up on this incline after making it so far, I dug my walking stick deeper into the ground as if the stick was going to take the last few steps for me.

Pressing ahead, I finally felt the ground start to even out. Reaching the top of the incline I was welcomed by a field of yellow wildflowers. In the center of this vibrant field the older boys already had their tents set up.

"Look who it is," Ryan yelled, as the others chuckled.

Unamused with their words, joy began sweeping through me as I realized I was now in the company of the more successful hikers.

Throwing off my backpack onto a bed of yellow flowers, I unlatched my tent and began setting up camp. Grabbing some food from my pack and seeing the final group arrive just as the sun began to set, I headed over to the fire to prepare dinner and exchange stories with the fast and slow groups alike.

After some much needed food and relaxation, I retired to my tent. Knowing the most difficult part of the hike would be in the morning, I closed my eyes and that night slept in the heights of heaven.

"Wake up guys, the mountain awaits you," Steve declared as he walked around shaking our tents.

This intense shaking of the tents took place for over ten minutes before I was fully awake. It wasn't long before I could feel the trails that I'd conquered the day before now conquering my legs. Slowly I rose. Reaching for my sleeping bag zipper I sat up. Grabbing my hiking attire for the day from my backpack, I laid back down and mentally tried to prepare for the final ascent to the peaks towering above my small tent refuge.

Hiking attire on, sleeping bag rolled up, I unzipped the front door of my tent. Slipping my feet into my oversized boots, I stood, stretched and took a deep breath of the cool, crisp air. A small campfire that acted as our oven for breakfast flickered, causing light to dance on the tents circling about.

I disassembled my tent, and joined the group around the morning fire. After eating the oatmeal I prepared for breakfast, I peered up at the twin peaks which seemed like they were within throwing distance.

With my heavy, slightly intimidating backpack lying on the rock next to me, I realized it was about that time. Reaching down and grabbing my bulky, off-balanced backpack, I threw it around my shoulders. Then picking up my trusty hiking stick, I was ready to begin the day.

The more I walked the better my legs began to feel. The steep paths the day previous prepared me for what awaited me on this day. With a new sense of energy flowing through me, I peered up at the lofty peaks standing over me time and time again.

"I am closer than ever," I said, beginning up the first large incline for the day.

The theme I noticed from the day before didn't take long to reappear. The fast hikers blazed ahead while the slower hikers were inching along behind me. I soon found myself as the lone ranger, walking the calm, quiet middle ground. Just me and nature.

Learning my lesson from pushing myself so hard the day before, I didn't attempt to keep up with the older kids and didn't feel as if I had to be faster than the slower kids. I found peace in each step I took, knowing that each one was a progression towards my goal.

After conquering the first steep section, the inclines only got steeper. Proceeding with one foot in front of the other, I did my best to notice my surroundings. Filling my mind with the various rocks I passed, the different plants I walked by, and the animals I saw. This slightly helped me take my mind off the challenging trail.

With my legs wobbling, I looked for a flat rock upon which I could rest and sip some water from my replenished canteen. Continuing up the incline, that rock soon appeared. Sitting comfortably for what felt like 30 seconds, but in reality was nearly half an hour, I began seeing the slower hikers appear a few hundred yards below me.

"Time to continue," I said to myself.

Appearing to be within arms' reach of Twin Peaks from my vantage point, I wondered if the older kids were already at the summit. I thought about the comfort they might be experiencing.

With these thoughts fueling me, I arose and pushed forward.

By filling my mind with thoughts of reaching the top, along with the idea that the older kids could currently be resting comfortably at the summit, my resting periods became less and less frequent.

After what seemed to be an eternity, two identical peaks topped with snow began to appear through the thicket of dense forest I'd been working my way through. A sense of appreciation swept through me as I saw my long awaited goal in sight.

Something within was telling me to run, but with the heavy pack on my back and oversized boots on my feet, I was unable to go any faster than I was already going.

One step after another, the trek continued towards the cool, snow-capped peaks in front of me.

"They're more beautiful than I could've imagined," I said to myself, not taking my eyes off of them other than to ensure I was stepping on solid ground.

The slick rocks, turned into mud and before long I was walking on top of snow. It wasn't as white as it appeared from below but it was snow never the less.

"I made it," I thought to myself, exhilaration filling my body.

I took a deep breath of the clean alpine air, filling my lungs full of success. The older kids, about 100 feet above me started tossing snowballs down towards me.

"The final obstacle," I said, laughing to myself.

This gave me the strength I needed to reach them and use my well-rested arms to bean one of them in the head with a slushy wad of snow.

"You may be a better hiker than me, but no one out throws me," I thought.

Making it safely to the top of these magnificent peaks, I looked out over the beautiful, lush landscape. I was on top of the world as I gazed down at the valley. My goals, these same peaks I spent years looking at from below, I now stood on top of. I was higher than the birds, floating with the clouds.

"What an incredible journey," I thought to myself, looking back down the trail which I climbed up so persistently.

"It's worth it," I said, unlatching my backpack and laying gratefully in the snow.

Now I sit here many years later, recalling that incredible journey within my mind. Though it was some time ago, I can still feel the exhilaration of the climb. I can still feel the aches of my body as I pushed myself towards the goal of reaching the top of Twin Peaks. My heart still experiences the joy of accomplishing such a huge goal I had set for myself in my younger days. The struggle, the pain and the risks were all worth it.

I embrace this experience and realize the importance of this journey. I learned that by staying on the path of our dreams, persistently stepping towards our goals, embracing the feelings of success and believing in each step, the achievement of those goals is possible and achieving our dreams is inevitable.

Let us reach a new understanding, realizing that when the present moment we find ourselves in becomes so complicated and frustrating that it throws us off the path of our highest self and takes us away from our highest thoughts, we have the ability to remind ourselves of this story.

Trekking up this mountain, aiming for a summit with spectacular views and great rewards, we will have to cross difficult trails, steep inclines and rough terrains. It is easy for us to look at these rough patches and stop or quit. It's just as easy to wait for someone else to solve our problems for us, thus becoming increasingly weak and overcome with frustration and doubt. But with our minds focused on a specific goal, there are few things that can hinder our attainment of that goal.

Enduring the steep and difficult inclines will always lead to easier paths above. All paths in this amazing journey of life are absolutely essential for taking us to our final destination.

Give thanks for your ability to live in this sacred moment. Be grateful for this sacred opportunity to climb into higher states of being.

Section 5

I Am

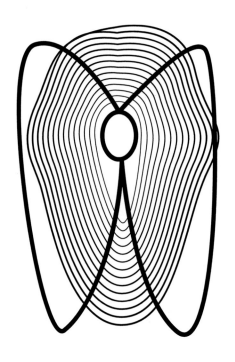

Unmasked and Free

The power of creativity infinite,
purpose is definite once we comprehend it.
Wisdom descends to the descendants of the sacred,
penetrating the heart so man can embrace it.
Taste it, feel it, begin to speak it,
transform it into actions so that others can see.
You are an example,
a sample of the Source,
consisting of,
this breath we take and steps we make,
the greatness we create
flows from our Essence,
finally escaping the masks.
The masks external factors place upon us,
as if the Omni forgot us and our Essence departed.

Unmasked,
Free.

Eternal Clock

Through the minds own design time ticks like the flowing river,
as experience delivers ideas formulating what one is here for,
the message is received through intuition,
interpretation of clairvoyant visions.

The past is the past, be here now,
don't look back,
many live trapped behind time's fictional mask.
The clock ticks on...
Transforming now into the future.
We count the hours, the minutes, the days,
in search of a freedom which we've already obtained,
in hopes to find a time when our own illusions stop,
a time found when we embrace our
inner
eternal
clock.

24 hours have no meaning at all,
be aware of now,
this is all you are

unfolding

All the Faces

Faces of hope, faces of regret and superstition,
faces of despair, faces of bad decisions,
faces of the system walk past faces of addiction,
faces of the unhappy amongst the faces of those who believe in their vision,
faces of the confused, faces of the youth,
faces of the tried and true smile at the faces of babies pure and new.
Faces of now speak with faces of the past,
leaving some future faces wearing yesterday's mask.
Faces of the suffering envy faces of peace,
a face with a smile is all the inspiration one needs,
faces of beauty, faces of misbelief,
faces different in size and shape, all faces unique,
all these wonderful faces looking back at me,
my own face gazing out of the coffee shop window as I peacefully sip my tea.

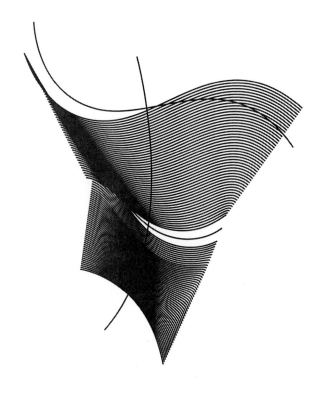

I Am

Why?
I ask why am I here,
why was I so aware in my younger early years?
Overpowering dilemmas,
the strength to persevere,
my five senses detect an answer but the response is still unclear.
My hands give thanks and praise for the day,
a welcoming environment I am hopeful to taste,
smells cascade combining with the sounds that are made,
my mind paints an environment as it relates to all I see,
sensory techniques, quietly speaking of how it all connects to me.

I am this day, I am this air,
I am this Energy, I am here.
Then why do I ask and receive no answers for my questions,
The reason I am breathing, the reason I descended?
I catch a glimpse of what it all meant,
as I spiral through a sequence of events,
connected to all I experience.
Within I is you, the One creator,
orchestrator of what my body detects,
constructor of my causes and effects,
assembler of the steps upon my quest,
giving me life,
I am this breath.

I am here because I am valuable,
I am gifted and I am needed.
The Essence of I,
eternally undefeated.

All Ways

When I close my eyes the whole earth is in my consciousness,
I must be larger than this earth to be able to encompass this.

Blue skies above me,
clouds pushed aside,
calm winds surround,
crowned with the Light of the Most High.

On the journey to understand who I am,
I ponder the many places I could start.

I have been told to live from my heart,
staying aware of this sacred place.
But what happens if that heart is to be replaced?

Am I still I?

Or is the energy that I am
traveling with the stars
that flickering light in the distance
is that who we are?

An illumination reflecting my minds design,
will that light always shine?
By observing only one's surroundings,
I was never found,
awareness tuned in deeper
broadcasting me into
here and now.
The all abundant energy
eternal and unbound,
spiritually connects us
to all we are around.
My limitation is imposed by fear,
it is this fear that causes the masses to stop here.
The moment I realized I was not stuck in this room in which I sit,
was the same moment I recognized Divine consciousness is all that exists,
Perfect in all ways.

Expression of Love

I am an expression of the upmost dimension,
the Divine reflecting.
The waves within my being, breathe out glory,
I inhale the present stories and chose my memories,
Perfection is everywhere, within the temple,
the consciousness, all creation
manifestations based on what I choose to take in.

Experience brings about wisdom,
knowledge points the way of peace,
speech reflects the thoughts one thinks.
I search for the missing piece
the missing link
me
is you
for I am light
as you and I are we,
breathe harmony, discover integrity,
open our Essence until we begin to receive,
our realm of existence expands through the Supreme.
If you believe then dream
the difference we see, rests solely in our mental imagery.
Please Think Love

The Greatest Treasure

We started from the moment all time began,
It never ends,
the past exists only in the minds of men.
We are all that is,
not in this flesh as it may appear,
our tears formed seas,
the air was formed through the breath we breathe,
our imagination brings up trees from small seeds.
So who are we?

I am you,
creativity at its highest potential,
monumental
we are the only treasure.

Think carefully

I Am That I Am

If I had the ability to see the future would I be called a dreamer?
If I was crucified for my fellow man would the scribes label me a believer?
If my life echoed love and hope, would the people say I lived with faith?
If I walked on water would people truly believe in my power to save?
Would those at the banquet find inspiration if I turned water to wine?
Would my legacy then eternally withstand the test of time?
If I organized millions to stand together and express love for our fellow man,
Could the world comprehend that the universe is our hands?
If I constructed cathedrals, great walls, and intricate stone temples,
Would one seek to tap this unbound potential?
If I never limit myself to a set path or plan,
would I then be able to tell you who I am?

The Lighthouse

I stand on the edge where the cliffs meet the water,
I shine bright speaking of what lies ahead.
Clashing beneath me turns rock into sediment,
carried out to sea, not to be seen again.

I must not be afraid, I know this is my purpose,
My light speaks truth that shines past the surface,
without this energy many would be lost,
sleeping as they walk, vanished and forgot.

My message is real, plain, and clear,
continue with positivity and you will always persevere,
I have withstood battles and weathered the most extreme,
courageously I stand for all to see.

I am energy
placed here for a reason,
an answer that has been received within.

I will continue to be motivation,
leading all in the right direction,
put your faith in me and you will not be forsaken,
my message will remain, I will shout it loud,

I am the lighthouse that stands strong.

TAPPING INTO SOURCE

The cool evening sun shone down upon a rugged beach that was lined with jagged rocks and surrounded by a lush landscape of grassy fields and colorful flowers. Water crashed against the rocks below, transforming the stones wave after wave. Shadows cast themselves across the landscape, leaving mysterious figures and designs atop the green canvas. Sparse grey clouds graciously floated through the sky, revealing signs of rain to come. Deep in the distance, a thick layer of clouds slowly formed, inching its way ever closer to the beach. Birds causally flew from rock to rock, hovering slightly above the waters' surface in search of fish. The sounds all spoke of nature's glory; waves, birds and a sea breeze.

This jagged beach front sat near a small village composed of settlers who ventured there after vast explorations in the years previous. The inhabitants of this village were composed of blacksmith workers, farmers, peasants, fishermen, deckhands, beggars and explorers. The village of St. Sierland was governed by the king's ambassador whose responsibility it was to forge a path through the new world in hopes of creating new settlements, acquiring more land and obtaining greater treasures.

This village acted as one of those new exploration areas. In St. Sierland, the seas were rich with fish, and great soil provided the farmers with abundant harvests. Being rich in these two essential commodities, St. Sierland became a hub for explorers who were preparing to sail across the ocean from its small ports.

Four men stood on the highest rock cliff overlooking the vast ocean ahead. Three of these men, in their late 30's, had been exploring different parts of the countryside for years. They eagerly awaited setting sail for their next voyage in hopes of finding an abundant land full of gold and treasures spoken of in the myths and fables floating through the town. The fourth man who stood there amongst the explorers in their late 30's was a young man named Ellander. Only being 19 years of age, Ellander had yet to sail anywhere. However, he too was swept away by these grand stories of abundance and treasures. He too, had a grand vision of conquering a land that very few knew about.

"So when are we leaving Jameson?" one of the explorers asked.

"4 weeks," Jameson, the eldest explorer, responded.

"Who will you be taking Sir Jameson," the youngest explorer asked.

"I will be taking the two of you," Jameson said, pausing for a moment, "And might let that young lad Ellander join us fo...."

"I appreciate you Sir Jameson," Ellander interrupted, "for your willingness to involve me on your voyage, but I've heard of a new place that few people know of. This place is untapped, full of riches, magic and power. Because of this, I'll be unable to join the three of you on this exploration."

The three explorers burst into laughter.

"Well, who's your crew? Who's going with you?" Jameson asked.

"Where I am going sir, for the land I seek, I won't be needing a crew," Ellander finished.

"Won't be needing a crew," the sounds of laughter echoed off the jagged cliffs into the clashing waters below.

"How can a young, skinny lad like yourself travel to a new land with no crew?" Jameson said laughingly, "You don't even know how to fish, let alone sail."

The three explorers laughed loud and hard about the foolish young man's plan.

"Just promise me one thing little Ellander," the youngest explorer said, "You better tell me once you've found this land, or your mommy will be worried."

Jameson doubled over, laughing so hard he crouched down to hold his stomach. The youngest explorer knew that young Ellander was new to St. Sierland and his mother was many miles away. With no family in the village, Ellander lived in a small shack in the center of the farm he worked on.

"I'll discover that land," Ellander whispered silently to himself, ignoring the laughter. "After all, I moved to St. Sierland to make a better life for myself, my mother and my brother. This new land is how I do just that." Laughter continued on around him, but Ellander refused to let humiliation fill his face.

"Which way is North again captain?" Jameson asked nearly crying.

"Tell me about this rich land that no one has ever heard of King Ellander," the middle-aged explorer said, guffawing at his perceived cleverness.

Ellander smiled, unwilling to let his determination fade.

"Gentleman," Ellander said, waiting a moment for the laughter to fade, "I greatly appreciate this conversation, I wish you all a great night."

"Our pleasure King Ellander," Jameson said, slapping the boy on his back as he turned to walk back towards the village.

Amidst a symphony of laughter, the last statement Ellander caught drifting on the evening air made his stomach turn in a cocktail of anger and humiliation.

"That Ellander is something else," Ellander heard, "He could never in his wildest dreams accomplish that big of a feat, he can barely handle the cattle on Sir Parrish's farm."

Entering the main entrance to the village, Ellander let the men's doubts bounce around in his mind as he ventured down the uneven cobblestone road.

"I left the village where my mother and brother live in search of better opportunities," Ellander muttered to himself.

"I don't care what anyone says, I will accomplish this," he said half-heartedly.

Walking through the dimly lit streets, Ellander couldn't get the heckling out of his mind.

"Why did I tell them?" He thought to himself, unable to pick one thought to focus on.

Struggling to maintain his firm determination, Ellander continued to the outskirts of the village where his small shack sat.

"I will do it. I know I can do it, I don't care what anyone else thinks," Ellander demanded, entering his small one-bedroom shack. "They have no right to tell me if I can or cannot accomplish this exploration."

After building a warm fire to heat his damp living quarters, he sat back, reflecting on how far he'd come.

Ellander left his family's village when he was 16 in hopes of finding a new place where he could begin a prosperous farm to support his widowed mother and young brother. He left his village with a small group of people who'd heard about the discovery of St. Sierland, the land of bounteous fishing and fertile soil.

Leaving his widowed mother and brother was the hardest thing he'd had to do, but he knew that if he stayed in the village, his birthplace, he would become like the other peasants around whom he'd lived, with no hope, no opportunity and doomed to a poverty-stricken life.

"Moving was the only thing I could do," he tried to remind himself, fighting back the tears.

Sending 50% of his earnings back to his mother and younger brother, his family was constantly on his mind. These thoughts motivated him to work harder on the farm.

Looking around his dark shack, he realized that his hard work was slowly paying off. Wiping the tears from his eyes, Ellander sat up and looked around, realizing that the shack he lived in was bigger than the house he grew up in.

"My hard work brought me this," Ellander thought, "I'll work even harder. I look forward to the day I can bring my mother to this land and inspire my brother to become a better, more affluent person than I."

Ellander finished his thought, arising to stir the porridge he was cooking on his small stove.

Preparing for bed, Ellander did his best to erase the laughter from earlier out of his mind, turning his focus instead towards this new land. Closing his eyes on his make shift bed next to the fireplace, he visualized this new land full of treasures, full of hope, peace and abundance. Forgetting about the humiliation he experienced earlier, Ellander discovered a deeper sense of purpose flowing through him.

"I know I can do it," he repeated to himself drifting off into sleep.

Awaking to the rooster outside his front door Ellander got up, preparing himself for the day. His workdays on the farm consisted of the usual, feeding cattle, goats and chickens followed by pulling weeds found in the crops as well as various household duties that Sir Parrish needed done. Thankful to have a job in the small, but growing village, Ellander worked diligently doing the most he could, the best he could.

As he did his work, Ellander made it a point to focus his mind on the voyage he was soon to set out on. So when he was feeding the cattle, he thought about the immense amount of cattle and animals in this new land he was seeking to discover. As he herded the sheep around the various pastures, he envisioned what the landscape would look like in this new land he was so eager to find. Throughout the day, Ellander was intrigued by each aspect of his work, inspired by each breath, trying to imagine what it would be like in this new land.

Completing his work that day, Ellander didn't return to the beach cliffs, instead he climbed one of the many large hills towering behind the farm where he worked. From this vantage point Ellander sat overlooking the countryside, spotting his small shack, the main street in the village and the ocean in the far distance.

From this vantage point, Ellander thought about the new land he sought. He thought of how abundant the opportunities would be there, thought of all the possibilities that lie in wait for him and his family in this new, uncharted land. Trying to grasp the vast amount of riches that wait for him, he had a hard time wrapping his imagination around the amount of abundance filling this new place.

"Once I discover this land, they'll know me as one of the greatest explorers of St. Sierland," Ellander said to himself. "I'll return to this village and then to my homeland to inspire countless others to voyage with me to this land of immense prosperity."

Inspiration swept through Ellander's body, filling his heart and soul. Looking out across the landscape, he was empowered. With this overwhelming inspiration and empowerment, Ellander rose and headed towards the village.

Walking through the increasingly congested village streets, Ellander was floating on a cloud of inspiration. Barely walking Ellander floated into a small pub where his co-workers and few friends hung out every day after work to drink away their woes. Entering the local pub, he joined his buddies who were already a few beverages ahead of him.

"Cheers Ellander," his friend Arthur said, "How are things lad?"

"I'm ready to hit it big," Ellander said in his still trance-like state.

"Hit it big," Tallon said, "Sit down. Tell us about this."

Snapping back into reality, Ellander sat.

"Four more drinks," Arthur shouted at a waitress passing their table.

"So tell us about this plan of yours my friend," Arthur drunkenly murmured.

"I want to let you guys know that I am now an explorer," Ellander began, "In a few days I will be venturing off to explore a new land."

"A new land?" Tallon asked. "I envy those explorers. I always wanted to head out on an exploration and discover treasure such that I'll never have to work again."

"So who's expedition are you traveling with Ellander?" Arthur questioned, "Jameson's? Sir Parrish's?"

"Neither," Ellander responded, "I am venturing off into this land of the unknown by myself. I've been preparing for this voyage ever since I left my homeland. I know great riches are there." Ellander finished.

"Alone," Tallon said jokingly.

"Ellander, you haven't even fished in the sea, how do you figure you are going to discover a new land full of riches?" Arthur asked as the table erupted into laughter.

"I've been preparing for this, I know I can make it," Ellander snapped back, "I don't care what you think."

"I'll get your grave prepared," Hodgman, Tallon's friend, said bursting into laughter.

"Rest in Peace Ellander. He who drowned before even setting sail," Arthur shouted, raising his beer mug.

"Here, Here," Hodgman, Tallon and Arthur clashed their mugs together, the sound of hysterical laughter muffled momentarily as they drank.

As the laughter grew from their table, people from around the pub started hearing the bold claims made by this young farm hand.

"Everyone meet my friend Ellander," Tallon shouted, now standing on top of their table, "He is setting sail to a new land in a few days. However, he isn't taking anyone with him. Take one good look at him, a farm boy turned explorer. Poor lad doesn't even know how to set a sail." Laughter rang through the bar, spilling out into the main street of St. Sierland.

"You cannot humiliate me Tallon," Ellander said confidently, hoping to dampen some of the laughter.

Slamming his hands down on the table upon which Tallon stood, Ellander pushed himself up, stood atop his chair and yelled, "My fellow villagers, what Tallon says is true. I haven't set sail before, but I am confident in my abilities and know that a great land awaits our discovery. I will venture to this new land filled with abundance and treasure, then return here for you, so that you too can experience this prosperous land of which I speak."

As Ellander finished his meaningful thought the pub became so filled with laughter that any hope of conversation was drowned out.

"Just wait! I'll return and you'll know that I am the one who brought you to this abundant land," Ellander tried to shout as he walked out of the pub.

Walking onto the main street just outside of the pub, Ellander began to feel the same feeling within his heart that he'd felt the day previous when the older explorers laughed at him on the coastal cliffs.

Heading back to his small shack, Ellander tried to grab ahold of the inspiring thoughts he'd discovered earlier that day.

"Why did I even say anything?" Ellander thought. "Everyone just laughs. I'll show them," he whispered, reassuring himself.

The closer Ellander got to his house, the easier it was for him to begin replacing thoughts of the heckling with the same inspiring thoughts that greeted him earlier in the day. It wasn't long before he was back in that place mentally where he knew that great abundance, peace and opportunities were awaiting him.

"I believe, regardless of what others say. I believe, despite my friends negative thoughts. I believe, despite the explorers heckles. I believe even if no one else believes," Ellander reminded himself, walking across the dark farm towards his shack.

"I believe, I believe, I know I will do it, I know I will find this new land," Ellander repeated to himself, stepping through his front door.

After building a small fire and reheating his porridge from the night before, he continued envisioning this new land, planning to set off in search of it in the upcoming days. With the right vision, excitement began flowing through him as he drifted into sleep that night.

The days passed and Ellander's voyage inched closer. He made it his goal to work harder than ever in order to prepare himself both mentally and physically for this massive adventure that he was to set out on the next day.

Feeling stronger and more capable than he'd ever been, Ellander spent his time after work walking through the village, quietly observing his own thoughts and feelings, recognizing the Life flowing through his body.

Ellander ventured to the rock-filled cliffs where he spoke with the older explorers many days earlier. Stepping on top of the lush green grass canvas, he eventually stopped at the cliffs edge and sat. Overlooking the rough ocean at the base of the cliffs, Ellander breathed, filling his lungs with the sea air, watching the birds hover gracefully over the surface of the water.

Sitting perched atop the jagged rocks in an inspired trance-like state, Ellander prepared himself for his voyage. He saw a ship set sail from the small port below, watching and wondering who the explorers were manning the vessel, where they were going and what the future held for them as the wind-filled sails pulled them toward the horizon.

Anxiousness filled his mind as he imagined all the things those explorers must be experiencing, and wondered what they were hoping to find.

Arising from his perch and preparing to leave back home for the evening, he heard familiar voices. Turning his head he saw the same group of older explorers he'd encountered days previous returning to the cliff's edge.

Unable to scurry away quick enough, the men noticed him and shouted, "Young Sink Ship, come tell us more about the voyage you're setting out on."

"Good day gentlemen," Ellander said as the men approached, still chuckling at their own wit.

"So when are you taking this trip?" Jameson, the eldest explorer, asked.

"Have you finally come to your senses and realized you don't have the skill level to even row a fishing boat into that sea?" The youngest explorer said snidely, pointing out to the rough ocean below.

"I am leaving tomorrow evening," Ellander replied, "I have been preparing myself for quite some time."

"Tomorrow night?" the explorers sneered in unison.

"You're more of a novice than I thought Ellander," Jameson said, peering into the young man's eyes.

"I am prepared and know what awaits me. I am eager to finally experience this new land," Ellander finished.

"I won't let you do this," said the middle aged explorer. "I'm not going to let you set off from this land only to kill yourself before you even leave the beach and end up as fish food."

"I appreciate your concern sir," Ellander responded, "But I am prepared for this voyage and no matter what anyone says or does, they cannot stop me. This new land is my destiny," Ellander shouted confidently.

The explorers laughed.

"Fine, just remember when your boat capsizes and you fall into that cold water that we tried to warn you," Jameson scolded.

"It is fully my responsibility," Ellander said. "I know what I am doing sir."

Nodding, Ellander wished the men a great evening and began walking back towards the village.

Stunned, the men nodded, mildly disgusted by the ignorance of the young man.

"We'll be at your funeral Ellander," the youngest explorer shouted after him.

Ellander continued walking, unfazed by the criticism.

Awaking early the next morning, Ellander rose ready to set out on his voyage. The day began like any other. After awaking, Ellander immediately tended to his work on the farm. Feeding the animals, leading the sheep and completing various other jobs around the farm, he finished his work early, returned to his shack and gathered the essential materials for his journey.

With the few belongings he'd grabbed hanging off his shoulder, Ellander walked to Sir Parrish's residence which was set atop one of the hills towering above his shack.

"Sir Parrish," Ellander gracefully spoke, "I will be setting off to discover a new land this evening."

"Get serious Ellander," Sir Parrish laughed, "You are not an explorer, young lad."

"Sir," Ellander continued, "I will be gone for some time, but I will return. I have asked Tallon to watch over my shack. Tallon also said he and Arthur will pick up the extra work around the farm until I return."

"If your work is covered, you may embark on your voyage," Sir Parrish said, bewildered, "But know that if your work does not get done then you will not have a job or a home when you return."

"Understood Sir," Ellander said, extending his hand out toward his boss.

After shaking hands, Ellander turned with his small sack of belongings dangling from his left shoulder and disappeared down the hillside.

Ellander traveled long and deep into a new land.

This land was a place Ellander had never seen. A place filled with treasures, opportunities, splendor, abundance, riches and wealth. It seemed as if the sun that shone on this new land was full of new life. Happiness was everywhere, peace was everywhere and love filled the air.

Ellander was in this place for over a week, exploring the vast beauty that filled the landscape. He filled his bag with riches and treasures that he would take back to the village in which he'd previously worked, where he would show the people of the magnificence he had found.

Ellander stood atop a rocky cliff overlooking the ocean. It was a sight he'd never seen, noticing a new beauty filling the water that clashed peacefully against the rocks below. As he stood on this cliff he heard familiar voices approaching.

"Ellander," the explorers yelled.

Ellander didn't move, just observed the immense landscape that lie before him. The men came up and surrounded Ellander. Laughter filled the air.

"I thought you said you were setting off on an epic voyage, filled with treasure and abundance," Jameson laughed.

Waiting for quite some time to reply, Ellander finally spoke. "I did. I ventured off into an amazing land full of treasure. It was beyond my wildest dreams. I breathed air full of love and peace. I am richer than I've ever been."

"There is no possible way for you to have traveled there and back that fast," the youngest explorer said, bursting into laughter.

"You're a crazy lad Ellander," they all exclaimed.

"A land full of riches beyond your wildest dreams," they chuckled even harder.

Unfazed, Ellander stood there in complete peace, unshaken by the words and laughter the men shot at him.

Turning his attention away from the vast ocean in front of him, Ellander peered directly into the eyes of each of the three explorers, acknowledging each and every one of them with confidence, respect, love and compassion. Noticing his serious yet calming demeanor, the laughter stopped. Looking deeper into Ellander's eyes, Jameson was the first to notice that the eyes they saw were the eyes of an explorer, someone who'd seen something that no other person had seen.

After moments of observing and recognizing each individual, Ellander spoke.

"This abundant place full of riches, peace, treasure and abundance, I have discovered it. This place however," Ellander continued, "Isn't found on any map. This place that holds infinite treasures and riches beyond anyone's wildest dreams is a place I have discovered within myself. Now I have returned to lead you to this place of endless abundance."

Amazement filled the minds of the explorers as they finally understood the voyage Ellander was talking about. Intrigued by this great young explorer, they realized that he had uncovered a land that was forever within reach, yet seldom explored.

Our mind is the only untapped land left. Only you can discover it. This land is greater than all the lands in the universe combined. It is this land within that makes up all the treasures of the universe. Explore within, and uncover the infinite greatness that awaits you.

Visualizations

INTRODUCTION TO VISUALIZATIONS

Your vision is a preview of life's coming attractions. The final section of the Book of Essence is designed to support you on your abundant journey inward, assisting you in honoring the Essence of your being. Use these Visualizations often to continue to recognize more of who and what you truly are.

It is imperative to remember that our entire experience of this life exists within our mind, our individual consciousness. As we expand within our own being, the reflections of that expansion begin to ripple into the realities of our current experience. Visualizing is an empowering way to begin that inner expansion.

The best way to do this is to get centered. Below you will find a detailed description of how to do just that:

I AM CENTERED.

All Visualizations begin with this statement. It's important to create a space of centeredness when beginning a visualization, prayer, or meditation. However, it's important to understand that you are able to center yourself as much as you would like throughout your day. It's not just limited to the meditation pad.

The more you do this, you'll eventually find that you are able to bring the calmness, the centeredness, and the peace from your meditative practice into the hustle and bustle of your daily life; providing you with the opportunity to live life from a centered state.

HOW TO GET TO THE "I AM CENTERED" STATE:

Sit in a comfortable position. It can be on the floor cross-legged (my favorite), in a comfortable chair, sitting erect, or you may choose a meditation pad.

While sitting, begin to recognize the support of your body. Feel gratitude as you give thanks for the ground upon which you sit, the air which you breathe, the environment in which you dwell.

Begin to focus on each breath (at times I count each inhale and exhale, up to 20 or so).

While focusing on your breathing, recognize that you are living. Truly recognize that you are living. Feel your heart beating, your lungs expanding and contracting, feel life moving throughout your being.

From this heightened state of awareness of the Life within, give thanks. Fill your body with gratitude.

YOU ARE NOW CENTERED.

Key Side Note: You can literally do this each morning when you awake, every time you start your car, every time you are around something or someone that brings out the best or worst in you. You can do this as many times as you would like throughout your day. The more you do this, the sooner you will find that this peace has always been within you. Life.

UNCONDITIONALLY LOVED

I am centered.

I close my eyes and take a deep, cleansing breath. In doing so, I feel myself becoming centered within. I allow all thoughts and distractions in the mind to slip away, as I begin to focus on my breathing.

I take three deep breaths from this awakened state.

I begin to turn my awareness within, to the center of my being. From this space, I let the love of all the people I care about and those who care about me flow into the center of my being. I think about my friends, my family, whether it be my parents, siblings, cousins, aunts, uncles, or grandparents. I let my mind scan all the great relationships I have in my life today. I think of all the relationships that I am grateful for. I bring this energy into my body and I am able to truly feel the love we have for each other. I can feel the love these people have for me everywhere I am. It surrounds me. I can feel my body bathing in this incredible love from all the people who care for me, all the people I care for. As I bring this love into my awareness I feel my body become refreshed, empowered, and inspired.

I slowly bring my attention to the Divine within, the Essence of my being. This Essence is all I am, is all that is, it is Life Itself. I am now able to understand that the Divine, this Essence, is this love. It is within all the beautiful people in my life. This love I feel from my loved ones is but a small piece of the love Life has for me. My inner eye begins to clearly see as I continue to recognize that everything in my life is the love expressed from the Divine.

From this state, I walk, live, and have my being, knowing that I am unconditionally loved and supported in all that I do.

DIVINE VESSEL

I am centered.

I take a deep cleansing breath, bringing my attention inwards, into my body. I send thoughts of gratefulness to all atoms, molecules, and cells of this incredible vehicle, the body I have been given.

I feel blood flowing through my veins, I feel my heart beating and my lungs expanding as I inhale air. I bring my awareness to the activity that is taking place within my own body temple and realize that I am under constant transformation. My cells harmoniously divide as my organs continuously renew into what the cells are becoming. My arteries act as roadways assisting blood cells in their flow to all the locations of my body. My brain cells awaken to their own greatness as my thoughts crackle with infinite possibilities. It's amazing that it's all happening within me, right now.

I am a Divine Being with a universe inside myself.

I step further into my awareness as I understand that though my body vessel may change and transform, there is an Essence within me, changeless and eternal. This Essence is that energy which gives life to all things, whether it be a planet, a tree, a human, a cell, or an atom. I know that this Divine Essence is what I am. I am One with this source of Life. For this is what enables my heart to beat, my mind to think, and my body to live. It is the space in which I have my being and It is within all the people I meet. I give thanks and embrace this sacred process that is occurring within me for all the days of my existence.

As I deepen my understanding this day and walk in the light of this awareness, I find oneness with my divine vessel and the Divine Essence through which my being exists.

BREATH OF THE UNIVERSE

I am centered.

I focus on my breathing. I take deep breaths, feeling my chest rise up slowly and then slip back down. I feel the cool air flow to the furthest corners of my lungs, replacing stagnate air that I am now choosing to release. I feel gratitude entering my body with each breath I take. I exhale love from the depths of my being, knowing that the breath I just released will be added to the immense universe in which I now sit.

As I continue to enjoy these deep breaths, I begin to ponder where this oxygen came from and its history. As I begin to ask this question I take another deep breath and peace coats my body, I become aware of this oxygen and recognize the beauty it contains.

I come to understand that this oxygen I breathe has been transforming through the ages. So as I take this breath now, I bring the universe within. As I take another breath, I bring the harmony, power, humility, and love of this oxygen into my body. Knowing that this oxygen gives fully of itself, combining and intertwining with elements which give rise to my body. I give thanks.

I now recognize that every breath I take is filled with this abundant perfection from the Essence of Life Itself.

CONNECTION TO THE COSMOS

I am centered.

As I exhale, I bring into my awareness this incredible planet that I live upon. I look out at the Earth and witness all the different kinds of life. I look above on a clear dark night and see hundreds of small dots illuminating the horizon and it helps me realize that we're but a dot when compared to the galaxy in which we sit. However, regardless the size of our planet, there's a magic, an incredible flow of life existing here and now. Somehow, I still know that as I sit here on planet Earth, I am connected to all the cosmos.

I am beginning to see more clearly that this universe in which I live is alive. Not only do I realize that it is alive, I understand that the same energy that creates those planets so far away from me is the same energy, the Divine Essence, which gives rise to all of life. As I look from this point of clear vision within, I see my connection to the furthest planet and the closest plant. I see the Oneness. I joyously join in the Oneness and inwardly see the beauty in all the people I meet and all the places I travel.

From this new state, I am able to see the Divine Being that I am.

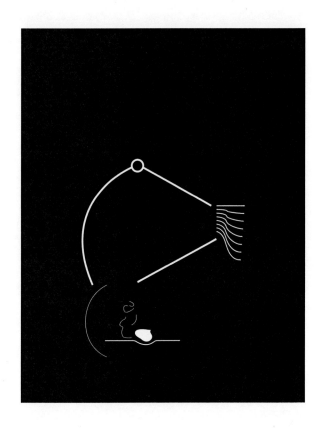

ONE WITH ALL

I am centered.

Today is a great day to be breathing, to be living. I am choosing to look deeper, to ask deeper questions such as:

Who am I?

Where am I from?

What causes me to rise in the morning?

How does our planet continue to sit in a vast universe, rotating faithfully?

And, how is the birth of a human connected to the birth of a star?

I continue to search the infinite that dwells within my own being. These deeper questions I sit with remove the masks that I have unconsciously worn in the past. I am beginning to see my connection with all things, my connection with all people in the present. I am able to look past the flesh and reunite with the Essence within. That which is Life Itself.
I am able to see this unity so clearly now because I recognize that I share this breath with my fellow man and woman. I walk on the same planet with all the animals. am empowered by the same sun that the plants reach for each day. I am sitting in a solar system that circles around the same star, while spinning peacefully in a galaxy which sits in an endless universe of other galaxies, energy, and life.

I feel my Oneness with it all.

I go through this day looking at my similarities with all the life I come across. Recognizing that the same Essence that enabled me to rise this morning empowers all the people I meet, all the plants I see and animals I pass to awake and be.

From now until forever, I move in this truth of oneness.

THE THREADS OF LIFE

I am centered.

I am beginning to see the importance of my life. I am beginning to see the role my life has on the planet where I live. I am able to see this by the effect I have on the people I meet and the environments I travel to throughout my day. I am able to see that I can carry myself with whatever energy I choose. I can be mad, depressed, envious, worrisome, joyous, happy, loving, or a mixture of many. It is completely my choice.

This is a great responsibility for me. I am learning that the more I consciously choose positive attitudes and emotions throughout my day, the more light, peace and hope I have to share with others. The way in which I live my life influences many things. This can be as simple and transformative as I would like it to be. It requires me to step through the darkness which I find in myself today, by so doing, I become the light which illuminates the path for all those seeking their highest self.

As I make my way through the dark caverns of my inner temple, I find love everywhere. It simply awaits my recognition of the beauty, peace, love, and wisdom that dwells within myself.

Now I can see that the same beauty, peace, love, and wisdom I am continuously finding in myself, I am able to find in all things.

THE POWER OF FORGIVENESS

I am centered.

I sit and recognize the breath that is flowing through my body. I recognize the thoughts as they quiet down within and begin to drift out of focus like a cloud does on a warm summer day. I fill my body with love. I begin at the top of my head, opening my mind and reaching towards the heavens. I fill my body with more and more love and peace each breath that I take. I keep the crown of my head open, receiving peace, wisdom, and love from the cosmos that harmoniously thrive above me. I balance myself with this magnificent earth that sits beneath me, extending the roots from the depths of my being into the earth. In so doing, I unify the heavens and the earth.

I bring into my awareness someone who I may envy or someone who may have wronged me in one way or another. I bring into my awareness someone who may have hurt my feelings, someone who I've had a hard time forgiving or someone I, myself, would like to apologize to.

I continue to keep the crown of my head open. Love continues to flow through my body with each breath I breathe, reaching deeper into the earth beneath me, stretching higher into the cosmos above me. I calmly bring this person, or persons, into my mind. I center myself back in this love I have created within me, the love flowing from the heavens above and earth below. I am full of this love and I begin enveloping the person(s) I invited into my consciousness with that love. This love is forever within me. I wrap this person(s) in this peace and love in a respectful manner. I do so as if I am honoring their Divine Essence. Tears, fears, and anger may be stirring within me, but I center myself in this abundant love that is forever gushing from the center of my being, making me unshakable.

I surround this individual with love and peace. I see their entire being illuminated from this beautiful energy I've shared with them. I can see past their fleshly appearance. I choose to see them as the Divine Being which they are. They too, are empowered by the same Essence which awakened me this morning. I would like to let them know that even if they never say sorry, or if I am never able to apologize, I will do my best to love them for the Divinity which they are. I will choose to forgive my fellow brothers and sisters for their trespasses because I know that at times I too may need to be forgiven.

In forgiveness, I dwell daily. Grudges, anger, fear, hatred and jealousy get quite heavy when I choose to carry them with me. I have found that forgiveness on the other hand, doesn't need to be carried, forgiveness is born within me.

CAUSING EFFECTS

I am centered.

I open my mind to this great power that I contain. I take another deep breath in gratitude. I give thanks for this abundant power within me. I further center myself and bring into my awareness this amazing gift of choice.

I recognize that I participate in the co-creation of my life with each choice I make. I further understand that each choice I act upon first begins with a thought which arises from my own body temple. I embrace this great gift and realize that I can use this gift of choice consciously, by choosing specific events and thoughts that will lead me to my highest purpose and best self. I am grateful for my ability to co-create my existence and gracefully accept the responsibility this sacred gift bestows.

It is my choice today to be the best that I can be. I choose to do this by making the best choices possible through the proper use of my mind and thoughts. This is a gift that only I can use for myself. As I continue to develop this gift, continuing to manifest the life which I desire, I effortlessly and joyously become an example for my fellow man and woman. The more I awaken to this great power of choice, the more I empower the masses to awaken to this gift that rests within them.

Each choice I make has an equal effect. I am the causal agent in my life.

INCREASING COMPASSION

I am centered.

I recognize my breath. I recognize the ground on which I currently sit. I gracefully and easily let my thoughts float through my mind. I feel peace, love, and life flowing into my body with each breath I take. From this space I am centered.

I open my inner awareness to the newness of this day. I open my heart to the purity of this moment I am experiencing. I open my mind to the endless possibilities, thoughts, and expressions that flow through my being. I stand in this Power.

I expand my awareness even further, and know that I have the ability to awaken. I have the ability to raise my own consciousness. I have the ability to live better, to live fuller, to be at peace with my life and my experiences. As I recognize this expansion and growth that is ever-present unto me, I begin to spark my potential into the darkness of my own ignorance. That single spark that occurs in me this day ignites into a universal event as I embrace the Source which I am from.

I have the opportunity to dwell in this inner realm of the soul, the resting place of the spirit, anytime I choose. This is a choice that only I can make for myself. As I choose this higher state of being, I understand that Love is the truth and my only true feeling. I could count for thousands of years and still not equate the amount of blessings I've been given. All these blessings flow from this Love.

I awaken to the awareness that I am not of this flesh. I am that which dwells in the flesh. I awaken. I am awake. I joyously shine my light to assist others in grasping the infinite within themselves and transcend my petty ignorance. I am here to bring a higher level of life to my world through the Love I uncover in myself.

THE PRESENT MOMENT

I am centered.

I open my mind up to the expansion of the universe in which I now rest. I honor the ground or chair on which I now sit. I take another deep breath and feel life flowing through my body. I get a higher sense of this Life flowing through me as I focus more and more on my breath. I sit in the magic of this Life right now.

I stand in unity with this Life that is flowing within. I realize it is the same Life that is flowing throughout the entire universe this moment. I celebrate the creative power this moment of now contains. I open my mind and see all the Life that is happening right now, as I sit, rest, and reflect. I feel all the Life that is happening within my own body and I look out amongst the planet and recognize that there is an incredible amount of activity happening now.

I open my mind further and recognize not only all the people living, moving, and working in this moment, but I recognize the trees, the plants, the streams and rivers, the oceanic life, mountains forming, minerals combining, islands shifting and seeds sprouting. I see this not just on a physical level, but I recognize and honor each atom, molecule, and cell within each piece of Life. I can see the harmony, the sacred order, and the love on every level.

This is felt within my own being.

I ascend further into the stars above me. I bring into my consciousness the immensity of Life that is occurring throughout the universe. Just as Life is happening here on our planet, there are countless other galaxies that have Life flowing through them. Right now, there are gases joining, elements uniting, comets soaring, stars illuminating, new stars birthing, new life evolving. I don't just see this in the external realm, I can feel the love, the respect, and the Life that shines from each atom, molecule, element, and mineral within all forms of life throughout the cosmos. Regardless of how far I may believe the Universe goes, I recognize that I share this present moment with it all.

All of Life is living together through this moment.

As I become aware of the infinite amount of Life that is taking place now, I begin to sense the Power contained in this very moment of my life. The more I honor and respect the power of this present moment, the better I understand all that I Am.

SPEAK LIFE

I am centered.

I bring myself to a place of peace, led by deep breaths that fill my body. I allow my mind to clear as I sit in Oneness. In this peaceful state that I have created, I open my mind to a clearer vision, a higher state within myself.

Centered, I begin to look within my own life. I look at my choice of communication and the strength that my words contain. I notice how many people in my life I've spoken with. I think of how many people I speak with on a daily basis and all the people I may only speak with once in my life. I understand that my choice of communication, the words I choose to speak, are of the utmost importance. I begin to acknowledge that my words act as messengers, actually entering into someone's mind and delivering my words based on the way I said them. Each word is filled with the emotion I put behind them as well as the thoughts I was thinking when I began to speak.

I am the one who commands these messengers, my words. I can command them to enter into the mind of another person and empower or enter into the mind of another and deflate.

I embrace my amazing ability to consciously choose the words I express to all people. If I look deeper than the physical realm, especially when talking with another person, I will notice that I can see this person as they truly are, beautiful and Divine. If I choose to recognize the Divinity in my fellow man and woman, then I must too choose to communicate to the Divinity that is within them. It is my responsibility to speak from this higher space within myself into the higher space within others. From this state there can be no words of hatred, envy, jealousy, anger, doubt, worry, or disbelief. When you know you are this Essence, this One Love, you then speak this Love to all.

I send my words out into the world to sprout into seeds of inspiration, motivation, empowerment, peace and love.

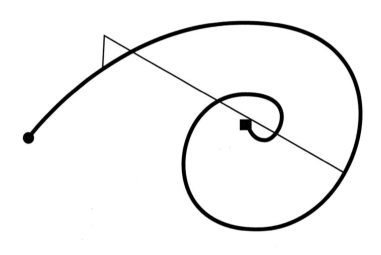

EXPANDING AND BECOMING

I am centered.

Have you yet to see the final place of your
journey having accomplished all of your dreams?

Visualize.

Have you felt the power so real
it can heal any injury acquired on the battlefield?

Believe.

Have you understood the energy possessed by man?
Success is destiny if we believe we can.

Awaken.

Have you realized we control and create the environment in which we choose to stay?

It is time.

Are you aware of the abundance surrounding us every moment?

Be grateful.

Grasp life in your hands, create your opportunities.

the universal piece of life
small, it rests inside
without there is darkness
through it there is life

invisible to the eye
recognized through the mind
connected to the spirit
from the soul it climbs

reuniting with itself
the light becomes brighter
uncovering truth
vibrations reach higher

embracing the gift of love
release desire
thoughts of compassion
consciousness inspires

peace fills the body
forgiveness cleanses the heart
awareness of harmony
life is our thoughts

What must not be forgotten is in truth, we all are
eternally connected,
One shining star.

Jeffon Seely shares his inspiration and empowerment
with the world through books, keynote speaking,
workshops, retreats, coaching and mentoring.

He may be reached via email or directly through his website:

JEFFON@THREEKEYLIFE.COM
WWW.THREEKEYLIFE.COM